Section 4

FISHES OF THE WORLD

——

CHRISTOPHER W. COATES
JAMES W. ATZ

Fishes—Their Whys and Wherefores

WHAT IS A FISH ?

ASK ANYONE what creatures live in water, and nine times out of ten the first answer will be "fish". A vast and colourful horde of other living things make their home in the oceans, lakes, rivers, streams, and swamps of the earth, but to man the fish has always been the most important of water dwellers.

And for good reason. Since before the dawn of history, man has relied upon the fish as food, wresting a good part of his livelihood from the water. He has found a thousand cunning ways to satisfy his needs with this creature, from making tools of its skeleton, a fertilizer of its flesh, a bone-building medicine of the rich oil in its liver, right up to using the fish itself as a decoration in his home.

Fishes dominate the waters of our planet. There are more fishes— and more different kinds of them—than of any other good-sized animals living wholly or partly in water. Today we are able to recognize more than twenty-five thousands of fishes—as many species as there are of mammals, birds, reptiles, and amphibians put together.

What is a fish? Don't suppose this question is naive. To cover so diverse a group of animals with a single definition—one that will include all the kinds of fishes and at the same time exclude all living things that are not fish—is difficult. Fishes are so varied in the nature of their bodies and the way they use their organs, that exceptions turn up for almost every characteristic of fishes in general. For example:

1393

a number of fishes have no scales; a few have no fins; a few lack jaws; some do not breathe primarily by means of gills; and others spend practically as much time out of the water as in it.

After gathering together a number of the features unique among fishes, and taking account of the exceptional fish that lacks one or another of them, we arrive at the following definition: A fish is a cold-blooded, aquatic vertebrate with gills and a two-chambered heart.

Like most definitions, this one needs some explaining to make it fully understandable. A vertebrate is, briefly speaking, an animal with a backbone, and this characteristic alone is sufficient to separate fishes from all the invertebrates (animals without backbones)—which include such creatures as insects, spiders, shellfish of all sorts, star-fish, and their relatives, all kinds of worms, sponges, and jellyfish— and also from the near-vertebrates (protochordates), the acorn-worms, sea-squirts, and lancelets.

The fact that fishes are cold-blooded, that is, have a body tempera-ture which more or less closely follows that of the water or air in which they live, clearly distinguishes them from birds and mammals. (We must say "more or less" because a very few fishes, such as the tunas, maintain a body temperature which is somewhat higher than that of the water surrounding them.)

The fact that fishes have a two-chambered heart also separates them from the amphibians and reptiles and from the birds and mammals— all of which have three- or four-chambered hearts. The gills, too, are an important feature of fishes. Although some fishes do not depend on their gills for breathing, these organs are always present, even though they may consist of only a few undeveloped filaments.

Fishes are aquatic, with no exceptions whatsoever. Those that spend hours or perhaps days at a time out of water, must still periodically return to that element to keep from becoming dried out. Some fishes can live for months without water, and a very few even for years, but they can do this only when inactive, in a state of suspended animation. All active fishes require at least enough water to bathe their bodies and keep their respiratory, or breathing, organs moist.

Actually, it is much easier to distinguish fishes from other generally similar aquatic animals than you might gather from what we have said. You can tell fishes from whales and porpoises by their tails; in fish the tail is vertical, like a rudder, while in whales and porpoises it is horizontal. A snake and an eel can be distinguished at a glance: the

THE
ILLUSTRATED ENCYCLOPAEDIA
OF ANIMAL LIFE

THE ANIMAL KINGDOM

The strange and wonderful ways of
mammals, birds, reptiles, fishes and
insects. A new and authentic natural
history of the wild life of the world

VOLUME 12

FREDERICK DRIMMER, M.A.
EDITOR-IN-CHIEF

GEORGE G. GOODWIN
Associate Curator of Mammals,
The American Museum of Natural
History

CHARLES M. BOGERT
Curator of Amphibians and Reptiles,
The American Museum of Natural
History

DEAN AMADON
E. THOMAS GILLIARD
Associate Curators of Birds,
The American Museum of Natural History

CHRISTOPHER W. COATES *Curator*
JAMES W. ATZ *Assistant Curator*
Aquarium of The New York Zoological
Society

JOHN C. PALLISTER
Research Associate, Insects, The American Museum of Natural History

ODHAMS BOOKS LIMITED, LONG ACRE, LONDON

*Colour photographs supplied by members of The Free Lance
Photographers Guild except as otherwise individually credited.*

snake has no gill-openings, but the eel has. Tadpoles have no paired fins, and this marks them off from all but a very few fishes—and these few exceptional fishes are so untadpole-like that they could never be confused. Recognizing fishes, you can see, is more difficult in theory than in practice.

WHERE FISHES LIVE

More than seven-tenths of the earth's surface is covered with water, and practically all of this vast area is inhabited by fishes. The seven seas, the many lakes, streams, ponds, and swamps all accommodate typical groups of fishes of one kind or another.

Ocean waters contain by far the greatest proportion of fishes—both in number of species and individuals. In the sea, fish are found from shallow, temporary tide pools down to the utmost depths of the ocean; in fact almost everywhere except uninhabitable regions such as the lower levels of the Black Sea, which are completely devoid of oxygen. Some fishes are what might be called "blue water" dwellers, living out in the middle of the ocean and never seeing or coming close to land during their whole lives. Others remain near shore, around coral reefs, or at the mouths of rivers. Still others live on the bottom, be it rocky or muddy, in calm depths, or near surf-washed beaches.

Freshwater fishes are subject to even greater extremes in the waters they inhabit. The streams of the world—from source to mouth— provide living places for various types of fish. Fishes are found in mountain torrents and sluggish rivers, ice-cold lakes and hot volcanic springs, foul swamps and clear, crystalline pools, soda-charged water-holes and acid lakes, sun-heated ponds and murky caves. Some fishes even make temporary pools their homes, and when these dry up, the fishes either travel overland to find water elsewhere, or hole up in mud until the rains come; they may also die, but leave their drought-resistant eggs behind to carry on the race.

Few of these waters are entirely isolated from all others, and there are fishes adaptable enough to live in more than one kind. For instance, a number can thrive in either fresh or salt water, or in places either warm or cold.

So it is not surprising that fishes, being subjected to such diverse conditions of existence, should show widely different structures and functions, and should vary so greatly in their life histories and patterns of behaviour. But this variety of dwelling places alone does not account for the diversity of fish life, because in a single, relatively uniform locality, as that around a coral reef, as many as two hundred species may be found—eloquent evidence that there are additional factors involved in the evolution of fish.

There is hardly anything that lives in water, either plant or animal, that is not eaten by some fish. Fishes prey extensively upon one another, too. Most bizarre perhaps are those relationships in which fishes make their homes inside living sponges, snails, bivalves, starfish, and sea-cucumbers, or in which they share the burrows of shrimps and worms, or live among the stinging tentacles of jellyfishes and sea-anemones.

We shall look more closely at the many wonderful features of fish life—the relationships between fishes and other animals and among the various kinds of fishes—in the "biographies" of various fishes, later on.

THE FISH'S BODY

A typical fish, such as the striped bass, is roughly spindle-shaped, tapering at each end. Its muscular, streamlined body is beautifully constructed for fast and efficient movement through the relatively dense medium of water. The rear end of the body, including the tail fin, serves as the principal means of locomotion through the water; its motion from side to side causes the fish to move forward. The caudal, or tail, fin plays only a minor part in this process, although it does make for more precise movement. The fins along the midline of the dorsal surface (the back) and on the midline of the ventral surface (the belly) behind the anus, or vent (called "dorsal" and "anal" fins, respectively), act as keels or stabilizers, and the two sets of paired fins, the pectorals and the pelvics (corresponding to the limbs attached to the shoulders and hips of other backboned animals) are used in stopping, turning, and other manoeuvring.

In the water, the fish has to move up and down, as well as from side to side and forward and backward; except for the birds and bats, few vertebrates face this problem. As a consequence, fishes have an extreme nicety of adjustment and interaction of fins and flexible body. Even breathing is integrated, because the discharge of water through the gill covers tend to move the fish forward, and so is compensated for— chiefly by movements of the pectoral fins.

HOW FISHES REMAIN SUSPENDED IN WATER

In order to remain suspended in the water without constantly swimming to keep from sinking to the bottom or floating to the surface, many fishes have bodies with nearly the same density as the water surrounding them. Flesh and bone are heavier than water, of course, but, to compensate for this weight, many fishes, the striped bass included, have a swim bladder, or air bladder, which is a long sac, filled with gas, between the stomach and the backbone. In some fishes

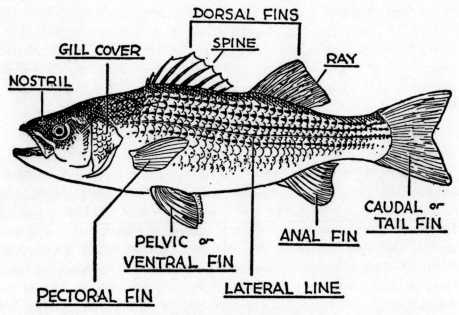

UNDERSTANDING THE FISH

This illustration shows a typical fish, the striped bass, with the principal fins and other external organs labelled. Spines are sometimes found in other fins beside the dorsal. Only the pelvic and pectoral fins are paired.

this bladder opens into the gullet; in others, like the striped bass, it is sealed off completely. In either case, however, the volume of gas inside can be changed to suit different conditions. Air bladders are also sometimes used as breathing organs, as aids in hearing, and in the production of sound. A good number of fishes get along without them, mostly bottom-inhabiting forms, but even some that live in mid-water, such as certain sharks and the Atlantic mackerel, lack an air bladder.

THE WAY IN WHICH FISHES BREATHE

The striped bass breathes by taking in water through its mouth and passing it through its gills and out under its gill covers. The gills are so constructed that they can extract oxygen which is dissolved in the water and throw off carbon dioxide into it. Several groups of fishes also have accessory breathing organs which enable them to breathe in directly the air above the surface. Such species often live in stagnant or warm water, where the amount of dissolved oxygen is low and that of asphyxiating carbon dioxide is high. Among these fishes are ones which have become completely dependent on their accessory breathing organs and drown if kept too long under water.

All fishes must eat, but do they drink? The answer is definitely *yes* so far as ocean-dwelling bony fishes are concerned, and recent experiments indicate that at least some freshwater fishes also regularly swallow water in addition to what they might accidentally take in while feeding.

A FISH'S SENSES

Some fishes are primarily "eye-minded", depending for the most part on their eyes for sensory contact with the world about them. The striped bass is one of these, and the pike is another. Other species, such as the brown bullhead and the sturgeons, are more "taste-minded" or "smell-minded". This type often has barbels, or "feelers", with which to explore its surroundings. Viewing objects through the water presents difficulties not encountered in air; nevertheless, numerous fishes show real ability to see sharply—witness the accuracy with which the trout or the bass strikes at the fisherman's fly. So far as known, fishes are also able to perceive colours.

Fishes have ears, although they are hidden away inside their heads. Like other vertebrates, fishes use their ears to keep their balance and to detect sound waves. Fishes are also equipped with a system of small canals that lie under the skin and communicate with the exterior by a series of pores. Part of this complex organ is visible externally; it is known as the "lateral line", and is quite apparent in the striped bass. It "feels" many of the numerous vibrations transmitted through the water, thereby acting as a sort of long-distance touch. Not all fishes have lateral lines, however.

In fishes, the nose is not connected to the mouth, except in a handful of species. Fishes use their noses only to smell, not to breathe—with the exception of the electric stargazer and its very close relatives, and perhaps certain eels. Smell and taste are rather difficult to tell apart under water; at any rate there is a lot of evidence that fishes can be acutely sensitive to chemical substances. Many of them have taste buds over much of their bodies, and thus are able to detect the presence of food even with their tails.

Usually barbels and other sensory organs are especially well equipped with taste buds.

BIRTH AND CARE OF THE YOUNG

The vast majority of fishes reproduce themselves by means of eggs that are both laid in the water and fertilized there. Their eggs are usually spherical, less than one-eighth of an inch in diameter, and may sink or float. A few kinds of fishes give birth to living young, and a still smaller number lay eggs that have already been fertilized while inside the female. Although most fishes show no concern toward their eggs, quite a number make nests for them, guard them, and otherwise care for them until they hatch. A few of these also watch over the fry when they hatch from the eggs. With few exceptions, it is only the male fish who makes the nest and performs the "nursery" duties; in certain species both parents co-operate, and in others the female alone cares for the eggs and young.

POPULAR NAMES OF FISHES

Many hot arguments have been held over the proper popular name for a given fish. It usually turns out that both sides were right; a fish having a certain popular name in one part of the country may be called by a different one somewhere else. What we call the zebra fish, for example, is also known as the lion fish, turkey fish, butterfly cod, devil fish, dragon fish, stingfish, firefish, and fireworks fish.

The better recognized a fish is, the more popular names it seems to have; for instance, no less than forty-four different names have been recorded for the well-known largemouth black bass. At one time or another this fish has been called green bass, white bass, grey bass, yellow bass, spotted bass, striped bass, straw bass, moss bass, mud bass, rock bass, river bass, lake bass, marsh bass, bayou bass, and cow bass.

It has also been called a green or white trout, a white salmon, a green or yellow pond perch, and a southern chub. Many of these names have been traditionally attached to entirely different species. Many are confusing in that a member of the freshwater black bass and sunfish family cannot very well also be a member of the perch or the salmon and trout family.

An effort to straighten out this confusion has recently been made by the American Fisheries Society, the Outdoor Writers Association of America, and the Board of Conservation of Florida, working through the University of Miami. Each has published a valuable check list of fishes that includes a careful selection of popular names. Since it is clearly impossible for us to list even a part of the multitudinous synonyms belonging to most fish of the succeeding series of "biographies", we have followed these authorities, especially the first, in our choice of popular names.

FISHES OF LONG AGO—
AND THEIR DESCENDANTS TODAY

Fishes form the oldest group of vertebrates, that is to say, they were the first backboned animals to develop on the earth. The earliest fossil record of them dates back to the Ordovician period, some four hundred million years ago.

These fish, which we call "Ostracoderms" (meaning "shell-skinned"), were heavily armoured and had no jaws. The head and front part of the body were encased in a shieldlike, bony, external cover. Most species were small, and all of them were certainly not "built for speed". They apparently poked along the bottom, sucking in dead organic matter for food, and depending on their armour for protection. None of these ancient fishes is alive today; they have been extinct for the last 280 million years. Their nearest living relatives are the jawless fishes—the lampreys and hagfishes—of the class Cyclostomi ("circular mouthed").

During succeeding millions of years other groups of armoured fishes appeared and disappeared. Sharks first show up in geological deposits that are somewhat more than three hundred million years old. Their descendants constitute the class Chondrichthyes ("cartilage-fishes"), which have gristle instead of true bone in their skeletons.

About the same time the first of the class Osteichthyes ("bony fishes") appeared on the earth. This group, which now contains the vast majority of fish species, differs from the others in having true bone in at least some part of the skeleton. Because of the various highly specialized members of the group, it is hard to find characteristics that are common to all species. All have jaws and at least one pair of nostrils, but some lack fins or scales; in fact, practically every fish characteristic is lacking in one species or another, or is so modified as to be hardly recognizable.

One very old group of bony fishes—that comprising the cross-opterygians (a name meaning "fringed fins")—is of especial interest, because it was from them that the first backboned land animals, the amphibians, evolved. Although at one time the fringe-fins were the chief animals of prey in fresh water, only two salt-water species are known to be alive today. These "living fossils" are the East London coelacanth and the Anjouan Island coelacanth. With their close relatives the lungfishes, the fringe-fins constitute one of the major divisions of the bony fishes, the subclass Choanichthyes ("nostril fishes")—so called from the fact that they, or their ancestors, had a nose that connected with the mouth.

With the exception of five species of lungfishes and two fringe-fins, all of the living bony fishes are included in the subclass Teleostomi ("perfect mouth"); these are the ray-finned fishes. The scientific name refers to the presence of true bone in the structure of the jaws and skull; the popular name to the structure of the fins, by which these fishes can be distinguished from the fringe-fins. Although a few of the ray-fins have fins with a fleshy base like those of the fringe-fins, the arrangement of the bones inside is fundamentally different.

One point concerning the evolutionary status of fishes should be emphasized. Although they belong to the most ancient group of back-boned animals, and a number of them which are still alive today can be called "living fossils" because of their similarity to ancient types, the vast majority of species are as up-to-date, geologically speaking or in an evolutionary sense, as any bird or mammal. Most fishes of today represent highly specialized lines of descent that were undergoing evolutionary change at the same time that the amphibians, reptiles, birds, and mammals were evolving to their present state. Therefore, fishes, in their own way, are just as "modern" or "advanced" as any of these so-called "higher creatures".

THE PROTOCHORDATES, MYSTERY ANIMALS

Earlier in this section we made reference to these near-vertebrates. Unless you are a frequenter of certain rocky seashores or have fished for the lancelets in China, you have probably never seen a protochordate. In fact, few people even know of their existence. Zoologists, on the other hand, are well aware of them, but in many ways the protochordates are mystery animals to scientists as well as laymen.

The protochordates are not fishes, although they live in water. Everyone has heard about "missing links" and how they provide key information about the course that evolution has taken. By rights, protochordates should be missing links. They have, at some time during their lives, a rod-shaped structure (notochord), the forerunner of the backbone. Thus they stand between the animals without backbones (the jellyfish, shellfish, starfish, insects, worms and all the rest) and those with them (the fishes, amphibians, reptiles, birds and mammals). But instead of solving the problem of how some backboneless creatures through aeons acquired backbones, the protochordates have simply created new problems of their own. Instead of being a key, they turned out to be a headache. In other words, careful study of these animals has failed to reveal the course of evolution.

But the exact location of the protochordates in the scale of life is mainly the concern of scientific specialists. These animals are also interesting in their own right because of the most peculiar lives they lead. They may be separated into three principal groups: the sea-squirts, the acorn worms, and the lancelets.

Sea-squirts are aptly named, for if you touch one it is likely to send forth a couple of small jets of water. Most likely you would mistake the creature for a bit of marine plant life or at best some sort of sponge. It is a small, sac-like object fastened at one end to a rock and bearing two small holes at the other. The body is encased in a jacket or tunic which gives it the appearance of a small bag and from which it gets the name of tunicate.

Sea-squirts or tunicates live only in the sea, many of them on rocks that may be exposed at low tide, others in deeper water, and still others in the water itself, floating free. One of the fascinating things about the fixed sea-squirts is that they start life as tiny, free-swimming, tadpolelike creatures which soon settle down, lose the tail and gradually assume the typical adult tunicate shape—or lack of it if you will. They spend the rest of their lives in one spot, more like plants than animals. Like plants, some tunicates can reproduce themselves by budding. Whole colonies arise from the buds of a single individual. Tunicates feed on microscopic organisms which they filter out of the water.

Acorn worms live in the mud and are seldom seen. Like the sea-squirts, they are strictly marine. They may be only two inches in length or as long as two feet, but they are rarely any bigger around than an ordinary pencil. At the front end, they have a rounded proboscis which fits into a collar, and it is from this structure that they get their popular name. In the manner of earthworms, although they are not worms at all, these animals swallow quantities of earth or mud from which they digest the organic matter, and, like earthworms, they leave their casts on the surface near the entrance to their burrow.

The lancelets are transparent, fishlike animals, two inches or less in length, which inhabit sandy beaches in many parts of the world. They spend most of their time hidden in the sand, only the snout projecting above the surface. Occasionally they dart about, but they soon return, usually burrowing tail first. Although they look a good deal like a small fish, lancelets do not have eyes or ears, nor do they have a brain, heart or skeleton. They feed on microscopic organisms which they strain out from a current of water flowing through the mouth and out past the gills.

Despite their small size, lancelets are so abundant at one spot near Amoy in southern China that they are fished for food. It has been estimated that about 35 tons are taken during a single season. This is equivalent to more than a billion individuals.

FISH ARE BIG BUSINESS

The economic importance of fish is greater today than ever before and is steadily growing. Statisticians predict that much of the vital protein food necessary to nourish our ever-increasing human population—of which perhaps half is underfed even today—will come from marine (salt water) fisheries. At present, approximately twenty-five million tons of fish are procured from the sea each year. Investigations of ways and means to increase this yield are now being vigorously pursued in many parts of the world. In the United States, the total estimated catch of salt and freshwater fish for one recent year was more than 3,850,000,000 pounds.

Fishing for sport has become enormously popular of late, especially in the United States. There, during the year ending 30 June, 1951, more than sixteen million fishing licences were issued, providing a revenue of more than thirty-five and one-half million dollars. Trade experts estimate that fishing for sport provides an income of about 150 million dollars each year to tackle manufacturers, boat captains, bait dealers, and others engaged in the business end of "fishing for fun".

A third industry connected with fish has recently become quite important—that concerned with the keeping of fishes as pets. One estimate places the number of people who maintain captive fishes in America at ten million. A large fish-importing trade has been built up, as well as the domestic breeding and rearing of tremendous numbers of small tropical freshwater fishes, goldfish, and aquatic plants. Along with this, there has developed an extensive tank-and-appliance manufacturing business. Little fish are now big business; approximately 150 different species of "tropicals" and forty kinds of aquatic plants are regularly available on the market today.

Lampreys and Borers—
Modern Primitives

THE LAMPREYS and borers are the most primitive of living animals with backbones. Eel-shaped, jawless, scaleless fish with a single nostril, they lack the paired fins we find in most other fishes. For feeding, they possess a rough, rasping tongue, with which they scrape away an entrance to the body cavities of other fishes.

In all, we are acquainted with about fifty species of these creatures (class Cyclostomi, a word meaning "circular mouths"). They range from six inches to about three feet in adult size.

All of the borers, which include the hagfishes and slime-eels, are ocean dwellers, and lay relatively large eggs with a protective, horny shell. Unlike the lampreys, they are seldom, if ever, able to attack living prey, but eat their way inside fishes that are injured, or trapped in gill nets (nets that catch on the gill covers when the fish tries to back out). The borers devour their victims completely, except for head, skin, and the larger bones.

The Sea Lamprey, *Petromyzon marinus,* is a repulsive-looking fish with a mode of life that befits its appearance. It has a long, eel-like body, covered with scaleless skin that grades from whitish on the belly to greyish blue on the back in young adults, older individuals becoming mottled. Its only fins are a small caudal (tail) fin and two small dorsal (back) fins. It has a pair of well-formed eyes, and behind each of these stretches a series of seven holes which lead into the gills. A single nostril opens midway between the eyes.

Instead of jaws, the lamprey has a round, sucking mouth, lined with more than a hundred sharp teeth and containing a pistonlike tongue also armed with teeth. With its sucking mouth the lamprey fastens itself on to a fish, then rasps a hole in it, and sucks out its blood and body fluids. Lampreys sometimes attach themselves to large sharks and to boats, and are capable of overtaking and fastening on to motor-boats travelling at fifteen miles per hour. Occasionally they attach themselves to human swimmers, but do not feed on them, although they have been known to cut out lumps of tissue from whales to which they have fastened themselves.

There are about twenty-five different kinds of lampreys, and they are found in both fresh and salt waters of many parts of the world. Those that live in the ocean, like the sea lamprey, go into fresh water to spawn. In the spring full-grown sea lampreys, ranging from about two or three feet in length, enter streams on the American Atlantic coast. They sometimes employ their sucker-mouths to ascend waterfalls and rapids, and always use them to build their nests. Both male and female co-operate in moving stones to form a depression in which the small eggs, sometimes more than 200,000, are laid. After one spawning, lampreys die. The young larvae do not resemble their parents at all and are called ammocoetes. For at least three years they burrow in the mud, feeding on small bits of organic matter that they sift out of the ooze. Finally they change into the adult form and go back to the sea.

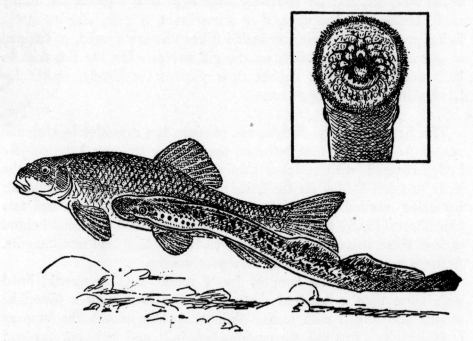

THE MOST PRIMITIVE OF ALL FISHES

The sea lamprey is in many ways the most primitive of living animals with backbones. It attaches itself to a fish, as in the picture (where it is shown on a white sucker), rasps a hole in the creature, and sucks out the blood and body fluids. The inset shows the sucking mouth of the lamprey, which has a large number of sharp teeth, and contains a tongue also provided with teeth.

Sea lampreys, however, can remain in fresh water all their lives, as is the case with the descendants of those that found their way through the Welland canal into the Great Lakes. Here the sea lamprey is considered a serious pest because it is believed to destroy large numbers of lake trout. In the ocean, too, this species attacks many commercially valuable fish. Although eaten today only in restricted localities, sea lampreys were considered a delicacy during the Middle Ages, and were used for food in the north-eastern United States until about one hundred years ago. Not all lampreys prey on other fish; the brook lampreys do not feed at all as adults, but simply reproduce and die.

FLYING THROUGH THE WATER

These cow-nosed rays, *Rhinoptera quadriloba*, gracefully flap their broad pectoral fins. They are smaller relatives of the devil ray, not exceeding seven feet in width. On the right rises a column of air bubbles, which serves to aerate the aquarium where the rays live. See *page 1417*.

MARINE HITCH-HIKERS

Two shark suckers have attached themselves to this sand shark by means of the sucking plate on the top of their head. Shark suckers will attach themselves to other large fish and vessels as well. *See pages 1408 and 1619.*

A SURPRISE FROM THE OCEAN DEPTHS

When fishermen captured this five-foot specimen in a fish trawl at 40 fathoms off East London, South Africa, they saved it as an oddity and it proved to be even more unusual than they thought. The East London coelacanth was identified by experts as a species of the fringe-finned crossopterygians which were believed to have disappeared from the earth about the same time that the dinosaurs became extinct. Fossil remains indicate that the fringe-fins were the chief freshwater predators for millions of years prior to that time, and the group is believed to have included the ancestors of all land vertebrates. *See page 1420.*

Sharks, Skates, Rays, and Chimeras

NOT EVERY shark is a fear-inspiring giant, yet some are even more than that. They range in size from two feet to about sixty feet in length. We encounter them in ocean waters throughout almost all of the world, but seldom where it is extremely cold. A few species run up into the fresh waters of tropical rivers, and three or four are regular inhabitants of freshwater lakes in Central America and Thailand.

Sharks are flesh-eaters, and some are extremely savage in their habits, as we shall soon see. Most of them give birth to living young, but a number lay eggs with horny cases; fertilization is always internal. You may be surprised at the enormous variety among the sharks: about 235 species are known.

Most of the skates and rays live in the sea, although the sawfishes and some of the skates go far upstream, and some of the rays live permanently in fresh water. The bodies of these strange animals are very much flattened, and usually their pectoral fins are so expanded they remind us of wings. The skates undulate these fins to drive themselves forward, while the rays flap them like wings, flying through the water. In size these fishes range from monsters twenty feet across the wings to those less than one foot in width. So far as we know, the skates lay eggs with horny cases, while the rays have living young. Scientists have named and described several hundred species.

The weird-looking chimeras are at home in the deep waters of the oceans, where they are only rarely seen. These blunt-nosed fishes attain lengths of roughly three feet. They lay large eggs with horny capsules.

The sharks, skates, rays, and chimeras are different from most fishes in a number of odd and interesting ways. For one thing, all of

them have gristle instead of true bone in their skeletons. They have
jaws, two sets of paired fins, and a curious covering of spiny scales
which gives the skin a texture like the surface of a file. Known as
placoid scales, these are found only on fishes of this group.

These creatures also lack the true gill covers of the bony fishes;
instead, the sharks, skates, and rays have from five to seven pairs of
gill clefts, each opening to the outside, while the chimeras have a
single opening on each side, formed by a fold of the skin—not a bone-
supported, muscle-controlled organ like the gill covers of almost all
bony fish. Sharks, skates, rays, and chimeras differ from the bony fishes
in several other fundamental ways, and are so distinct that some zoologists do not consider them to be fishes at all. We place them in a
class by themselves—the Chondrichthyes, a name meaning "gristle
fishes".

The Sand Shark, *Carcharias taurus*, is one of the commonest sharks
of the Atlantic seaboard. It is of little economic importance, however,
as a source of food, leather, or Vitamin A (from the liver). Typically
sharklike in appearance, it has a prominent snout, five gill-slits on
either side behind the eyes, an undershot jaw ringed with several
rows of sharp triangular teeth, and a tail with the upper lobe much
longer than the lower one. Predominantly light bronze in colour, its
rough skin, called "shagreen", has a metallic lustre when viewed
under water.

A number of species of sharks are dangerous to man; but the sand
sharks look more sinister than they really are, for they have never
been known to attack human beings. Their relative, the grey nurse of
Australia, has a very bad reputation, though, and has contributed its
share to the more than two hundred recorded shark attacks from
that continent for the years 1840 to 1940. From 1919 to 1949 inclusive,
seventy-seven authenticated shark attacks on Australian swimmers
and bathers are on record, in addition to thirty-three on professional
divers. More than two-thirds of the swimmers and bathers died from
the wounds they received. (The grey nurse is only a distant relative
of the nurse shark of Florida and the West Indies.)

The largest sand sharks on record measured almost eleven feet in
length, but the species does not feed on large prey, voraciously eating
many kinds of smaller fishes instead.

Females give birth to living young, a single one at a time, which is especially well developed at birth. Evidence indicates that the single foetus actively swims about inside the reproductive tract of its mother and that it feeds upon undeveloped eggs that apparently are specially shed into the uterus to provide nourishment for it.

The Mako, *Isurus oxyrinchus*, is a savage, streamlined shark of the warm Atlantic, renowned for the fighting qualities it shows when hooked. Most game fishermen regard it and its close relative, *Isurus glaucus* from the Pacific and Indian Oceans, more highly than any other shark. These species take rapidly moving bait, and then swim fast and hard with it, sometimes leaping as high as ten feet or more out of the water in their efforts to escape. They are also known to attack deliberately the man or boat that has them fast. The record Pacific mako was twelve feet long and weighed one thousand pounds. The Atlantic form is said to reach thirteen feet.

Makos are eaters of fish and can capture speedy ones like mackerel. They attack larger fish, too. The Atlantic mako fights with the swordfish, and whole swordfish as well as many pounds of swordfish flesh have been found in its stomach. In the Pacific, makos fight with the black marlin.

The Great White Shark, *Carcharodon carcharias*, is also called "the man-eater", a title that it well deserves, since it is undoubtedly the most dangerous of all sharks. Not only does it maim or kill bathers, but without provocation it will sometimes attack small boats. Few living creatures are safe from its huge appetite. Sea lions, seals, sea turtles, sharks, tuna, and a large variety of other fishes have been found

THE MOST DANGEROUS OF ALL SHARKS

The great white shark is known as "the man-eater". It occasionally injures or kills swimmers, and sometimes attacks boats. Its appetite is huge: sea lions, seals, and other large creatures have been found in the stomach of the shark. However, the piranha of South America is a more dangerous fish than this one.

—sometimes in a whole condition—in white sharks' stomachs. This shark also eats garbage and offal, at least occasionally.

The white shark inhabits temperate and tropical oceans all over the world, coming near shore fairly frequently in some regions.

One specimen was thirty-six and one-half feet long, but mature females are usually about fifteen feet long, and few individuals are found larger than this. A twenty-foot specimen weighed seven thousand pounds. The females bear living young.

The Thresher Shark, *Alopias vulpinis*, has an enormously elongated upper lobe of its tail fin which is often longer than all the rest of its body. This fin is apparently used in capturing prey. "Herding" a school of fish, the thresher swims round and round them, all the while splashing with its great tail. Gradually it forces them closer and closer together, and finally goes in for the kill. Sometimes two threshers will work together in this fashion. Occasionally, the tail is used to strike prey such as sea birds and fish. The old belief that the thresher shark teams up with the swordfish to attack whales is untrue.

This temperate and tropical species occurs in the Atlantic and eastern Pacific, but whether the form found in the western Pacific and Indian oceans is the same species or not is still undecided. Thresher sharks grow to a length of twenty feet or more, about half of which is composed of the tail. The females bear living young, two to four at a time, about three feet long.

Threshers are harmless to man, although they sometimes cause trouble by becoming entangled in fishing nets.

The Nurse Shark, *Ginglymostoma cirratum*, is a sluggish species that spends much of its time lying quietly on the bottom in the shallow waters of the tropical Atlantic. It is well known in Florida, where it is extensively fished for its hide, considered the best from any American shark for the production of leather.

Nurse sharks have large broods, as many as twenty-six young being born at a time. Newly born nurse sharks are less than a foot in length and generally show numerous spots that are usually lost as they grow up. Their ground colour ranges from gold to light brown. Although nurse sharks mature at about five feet, individuals as long as fourteen feet have been caught. They feed mostly on creatures like crabs, shrimp, spiny lobsters, squid, and sea urchins, and on small fish.

The Whale Shark, *Rhincodon typus*, is the largest of living fishes. Accurately measured specimens forty-five feet long are on record and some of sixty feet have been reliably reported. No one knows just how much such monsters weigh, but the estimated weight of a thirty-eight-foot example was nearly 26,600 pounds.

Found in all tropical seas, the whale shark occasionally ventures into temperate waters. It sometimes gathers in schools. Often it basks or feeds at the surface, and is so fearless or lazy, that it is sometimes rammed by ships.

The whale shark eats only smaller invertebrates and fishes. It has a large mouth with very small teeth and a strainer-like apparatus at the gills. Swimming open-mouthed through schools of little fish or aggregations of other small sea animals, the whale shark engulfs them. The water is then forced out through its gills, and the animals are caught on the specially contrived gill arches which act like sieves. There are also reports that this shark feeds in a vertical position, head up, and that it sucks in its prey.

The whale shark's back and sides are distinctively marked with round white or yellowish spots that show up plainly against the dark grey or brown of the skin.

The Smooth Dogfishes, *Mustelus canis* of the western Atlantic and *Mustelus californicus* of the eastern Pacific, are small sharks that attain lengths of about five and two and one-half feet, respectively. They do not inhabit the open sea, but usually remain quite near shore.

What we say here applies to the Atlantic species, but the Pacific one is undoubtedly quite similar. Crabs and lobsters are its chief food, but small fish, worms, squid, and other molluscs are also eaten. Garbage is taken if available. Dogfish have about six rows of flattened, pavement-like teeth, employed for crushing rather than shearing as are the more pointed teeth of many sharks. Scientists have shown, by marking individual teeth in the rear rows, that the dogfish's back teeth gradually move forward, replacing those lost at the front edge of the mouth. Since new ones are constantly being formed, to move forward as those in front break off or are worn away, the shark has a never-ending supply of teeth. The sand at the bottom of the shark tank in the old New York Aquarium was filled with hundreds of discarded teeth.

Other experiments have shown that the smooth dogfish seeks its prey by smell rather than sight, even though it has well-developed eyes. This is probably true of many other kinds of sharks, but whether it holds for the fast-swimming oceanic ones is questionable.

Some sharks lay large eggs covered with horny capsules. In others the eggs hatch while still inside the mother, and the young sharks complete further development before being liberated. In the smooth dogfish, which produces living young, there is an intimate, placenta-like union between the bloodstreams of the mother and her offspring, by which the embryo is provided with food and other necessities in a way similar to that in the mammals. The period of development within the mother is about ten months, and the litters of four to twenty baby dogfish, about fourteen inches long, are born in late spring and early summer. Since smooth dogfish are of little commercial importance and are believed to be destructive to other fishes, their abundance is sometimes an annoyance to fishermen.

The Tiger Shark, *Galeocerdo cuvier,* occurs in tropical oceans all over the world, and strays into temperate waters during the summer. No one is sure whether its popular name arises from its voracious habits and prominent, sickle-shaped teeth, or from the stripes and blotches displayed by smaller specimens. At any rate, tiger sharks are considered the most dangerous species in some areas, and are proved man-eaters around Australia.

Tiger sharks up to thirty feet in length have been reported, but the longest on fully authenticated record was an eighteen-foot specimen. When born they are about one and one-half feet long. The size of litter varies greatly; from ten to eighty-two young have been found in various females.

Most remarkable are the feeding habits of tiger sharks; practically everything edible—and much that is not—has been found in their stomachs. Their food ranges in size from small crabs to giant sea turtles and other large sharks. Spiny lobsters, horseshoe crabs, snails, octopuses, squid, fishes of all sorts, sea snakes, birds, and sea lions are all eaten by them. They capture sting rays which often leave their spines embedded in the shark's jaws. All kinds of offal are eagerly swallowed, including the heads and hoofs of cows and horses, and whole dogs, cats, and goats; even human corpses. Such indigestible things as old boots and clothes, tin cans, and sacks of coal have also been taken from their maws.

This abundant species is fished for its hide and also, to some extent, for its liver. As with numerous other sharks, its flesh is palatable and is used for food in certain localities.

The Soupfin Shark, *Galeorhinus zyopterus*, from the coast of California and Baja California, has long been well known to the Chinese, who consider its fins superior to almost all others as an essential ingredient of certain soups. The fins are cut off and thoroughly dried, in which condition they can be sent to market. Before they are used, they are soaked in warm water, and the cartilaginous rays, that in life gave the fin its strength, are separated from the flesh. Then these rays are sliced up and boiled with meat, chicken, vegetables, and so forth, to make soup.

Not until 1937 did the soupfin shark become generally known. At that time an intensive fishery for this species was instituted to obtain its liver, which had been found to be extraordinarily rich in Vitamin A. Since soupfin livers sold for as much as thirteen dollars a pound, and an average female's liver might weigh as much as fifteen pounds, small fortunes were made on a few boatloads of these sharks. Within three years, however, the number of sharks taken fell off to such an extent that many fishermen had to abandon the fishery. It is believed most probable that this reduction in numbers may have resulted from over-fishing, because the soupfin shark is apparently a slow reproducing and maturing species.

Male soupfin sharks mature at a length of about five feet, the females at a somewhat larger size. The young are born alive, and an average brood consists of thirty-five individuals.

Other species of sharks are also important for the considerable amounts of Vitamin A that are contained in the oil of their livers.

The Hammerhead Shark, *Sphyrna zygaena*, has one of the strangest heads found among fishes. Its skull is flattened into two long, narrow, squared-off projections, at the extreme ends of which are located the eyes and nostrils. No one has been able to explain the utility of this bizarre arrangement except that the placing of the paired sense organs farther apart may allow more accurate location of prey or enemies—much in the way that a wider base between two observation points permits more accurate range-finding for artillery.

The food of hammerhead sharks consists mostly of various fishes, including its own kind, other sharks, skates, and sting rays. There are several authenticated accounts of hammerheads attacking human bathers. Since they reach a length of thirteen feet, they are capable of doing considerable harm. In the shark fisheries of the West Indies and Florida, hammerheads yield both leather and liver oil. As many as thirty-seven embryos have been found in a single female. The young are about twenty inches long, and their "hammers" are folded back alongside the body to make birth easier.

A SHARK WITH A HEAD LIKE A HAMMER

The hammerhead shark, with one of the oddest heads in the finny kingdom, is truly a weird-looking creature; the eyes and nostrils are in the two long, squared-off projections of the skull. Hammerheads grow to thirteen feet in length, and occasionally attack swimmers. Two sharks are shown here with their prey, a cownose ray.

In the Atlantic, there are five species of hammerheads, but exactly how many exist in the rest of the oceans is not known.

The Little Skate, *Raja erinacea*, is the best known of the half-dozen species of skates that are found off the north-eastern coast of the United States. Like practically all skates, it lives mostly on the bottom and the greater part of its food consists of bottom-inhabiting animals such as crabs, shrimps, worms, sea squirts, bivalves, squid, and small fishes. It has numerous rows of small, rounded teeth set in a pattern resembling a tile pavement.

Skates are relatives of the sharks, much flattened from back to belly, with a roughly triangularly shaped body, and a long, thin tail. The large triangular pectoral fins, extending out on either side of the body, are the principal means of locomotion. These fins are undulated from front to rear, not flapped like wings as are those of some rays. The more or less rigid tail, with two small fins attached at its end, acts as a steering device to a certain extent.

The eyes are located quite close together on top of the head, while the mouth is underneath. The gill slits are also on the under-side. Instead of taking water in through the mouth and passing it out through the gill slits, as do the sharks during breathing, skates use their spiracles, which are two valved openings just behind the eyes. Water enters through the spiracles and passes out through the gill slits. Thus the problem of remaining on the bottom and inhaling without taking in debris—as would happen if the mouth were used—is solved.

The little skate is usually not more than twenty inches long, but may attain a length of two feet. Females lay eggs enclosed in a rectangular, blackish, leathery case, measuring about one and three-quarters by one and three-eighths inches, at each corner of which a thin, hook-shaped prong is attached. Similar egg cases are laid by other skates. They are sometimes found washed up on the beach and called "mermaids' purses". The eggs of the little skate are laid during the late spring and summer, and probably take several months to hatch.

There are seventy-five or more skates belonging to the genus *Raja*, and they inhabit most of the world's cool seas. Some of them occur in quite deep water. The largest species are about eight feet long.

The Atlantic Torpedo, *Tetranarce occidentalis*, and the **Pacific Torpedo,** *Tetranarce californica*, possess powerful electric organs that are strong enough to knock a man off his feet in certain circumstances. At the New York Aquarium, we measured the electrical discharges of a large local specimen and found them to be about two hundred volts and 1,600 watts. There is no doubt that such electrical powers are an excellent means of defence. It is believed that torpedoes also use their electricity to obtain food, by stunning fishes and other creatures before eating them, because relatively large fish have been found in their stomachs without a single mark on their bodies. Only by shocking them into insensibility could the torpedoes have over-powered these fish without damaging them in any way. Moreover, a Neapolitan species of electric ray has been observed shocking mullet into insensibility and then swallowing them whole.

In appearance torpedoes are distinguished from other rays by their round, disclike body, large tail fin, and soft naked skin. Some of them are said to attain weights of two hundred pounds, but the average Atlantic torpedo weighs about thirty pounds. Weights of more than fifty pounds have been recorded for the Pacific torpedo. Torpedoes are born alive and are capable of producing electricity even before birth. There are quite a number of different kinds of electric rays, most of them found in tropical seas.

The Sawfish, *Pristis pectinatus,* that occurs on the south-eastern and Gulf coasts of the United States, has a snout elongated into a flat, blunt blade, on each side of which is a single row of twenty-four to thirty-two strong, sharp teeth. This sawlike structure is about a third as long as the fish's body and is a formidable weapon in even a small specimen. In the largest ones of twenty feet, it may be a foot wide at its base and six feet long, with teeth projecting well over two inches on either side.

The mouth of the sawfish is located on the underside of the head and is equipped only with small blunt teeth. It is the "saw" which is used to obtain food. With a nicely gauged sideswipe the sawfish impales a fish on one of the teeth, then swims to the bottom with it and there scrapes it off, quickly swimming over the fish to engulf it—before it can recover, should it not be completely incapacitated.

The "saw" may also be used in a more haphazard fashion, the saw-fish swimming into a school of fish and rapidly striking from side to side. The dead or injured fish can then be devoured more or less at leisure. Sawfish have also been reported as rooting out crustaceans and other invertebrates with the "saw".

Sawfish live in shallow, tropical, salt waters and the brackish ones around tidal inlets and river mouths. They also travel upstream into fresh water well beyond the region of tidal influence. They give birth to broods of as many as twenty young, which are born fully armed with a "saw"! At this time, however, it is soft and flexible and covered with a membranous sheath.

There are about six different kinds of sawfishes. Although they have a sharklike body, sawfishes are really rays, as can be seen by the location of their gill openings, which are underneath the head rather than on the sides, as in the sharks.

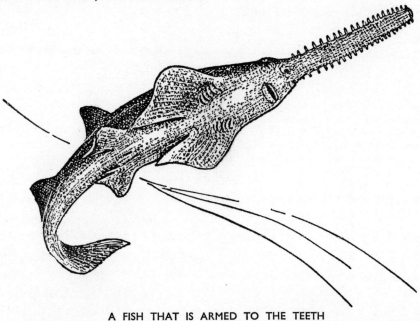

A FISH THAT IS ARMED TO THE TEETH

The sawfish uses its "saw" to catch its food. It impales a fish on one of the teeth, then scrapes it off, and swallows it before it can revive. Also, the sawfish swims into a school of fishes, striking them down left and right, thus getting more food. Even the young are born fully armed with a "saw".

The Sting Ray, *Dasyatis centrura,* hides at the bottom of seas, bays or rivers, its flattened disc-shaped body concealed by sand or silt and by its camouflaging coloration. When stepped on by some unwary person, the sting ray quickly swings its long, flexible tail up and around so that it drives into the leg of the unfortunate person a spine that is toothed like a saw. This spine is located on the top surface of its tail, halfway between the base and tip. The excruciating pain that almost invariably follows such an injury is caused by some type of poison that the spine introduces into the wound. Pain, swelling, dizziness, and nausea may be so intense that hospital treatment is necessary. In a few instances death is said to have resulted.

There are several dozen different species of sting rays, and they are found in all warm seas and in a number of tropical rivers. They range in size from a giant Australian form, that attains weights of about 750 pounds, to small freshwater ones that are the size of a pancake. The Sting ray, *Dasyatis centrura*, which is the one most commonly seen on the north-eastern coast of the United States, reaches a length of twelve feet, although specimens over six feet long are rare. So far as known, all sting rays have living young.

THE STING RAY AND ITS POISONOUS SPINE

Sting rays are found in warm seas and tropical rivers. In Australia, one sting ray grows to 750 pounds; freshwater rays, however, are much smaller. Halfway down its tail the sting ray has a spine with teeth like a saw, which it drives into the leg of anyone who steps on it. Poison is injected into the wound, causing intense pain and, occasionally, death.

The Devil Ray, *Manta birostris*, grows to weights of more than three thousand pounds, and is the largest of all the rays. It has a diamond-shaped body that may be twenty feet across from wing-tip to wing-tip, a long thin tail, and a pair of prominent "horns" projecting out from the head just in front of the eyes. These "horns" are really a pair of fins, called "cephalic" fins. They probably help the devil ray in obtaining the small sea creatures upon which it feeds.

Devil rays inhabit the warmer ocean waters. They apparently spend a good deal of time at or near the surface, "flying" through the water by slowly and gracefully flapping their great triangular "wings", or lying quietly, basking in the sun. Their common name gives a wrong idea of their habits, for they have never been known to harm a man or a boat deliberately, although they have capsized or demolished a number of boats in their Herculean efforts to escape when harpooned. Perhaps it is their forbidding appearance and great size that have given them the name of devil ray and made them much feared.

The female devil ray has a single large youngster at a time. One eighteen-foot, twenty-three-hundred-pound female which was caught, contained a young devil ray just about to be born; the young one weighed twenty-eight pounds.

Fringe-Finned Fishes and Lungfishes —Among Earth's Greatest Oddities

THESE STRANGE creatures are among the most fascinating oddities on earth. Their forerunners, the ancient fringe-finned fishes (crossopterygians) were at one time the chief animals of prey in fresh water. There were great numbers of them, and they throve for untold ages. But they died out millions of years ago. Or that, in any event, was the opinion of scientists until two were discovered alive in ocean waters quite recently.

Why should we dwell on these fishes of ages past? They are of great scientific interest, since it was from them that all land animals with backbones—the amphibians, reptiles, birds, and mammals—developed.

In these ancient types, we find that the paired fins, and sometimes the other fins, too, consist of fringed lobes. The rays and membrane of the fins are attached to a fleshy, scale-covered base, which contains supporting bones. These bones are so arranged that with relatively little change they could have become the support of a limb instead of a fin. Many fossil fringe-fins used the air bladder as a lung to breathe atmospheric air. These are two reasons why we believe the fringe-fins were the ancestors of the first backboned land animals, the amphibians.

The lungfishes are in several ways similar to the fringe-fins, but differ from them in the way the jaws are attached to the skull and in other characteristics. After studying the lungfishes and comparing them with fossils, some experts have come to the conclusion that the lungfishes are an offshoot of the fringe-fins that has become degenerate in a number of ways. Lungfishes have lobe-shaped paired fins, which may, however, be no more than mere ribbon-like structures, as in the African and South American species living today. They also have nostrils that open into the cavity of the mouth and an air-bladder that serves as a lung. Strangely enough, they do not breathe air through their nostrils, however, apparently using them only for smelling underwater. Many of the internal structures of the lungfishes resemble the ones in amphibians.

The lungfishes of today are but a remnant of those that lived in the past. Five species are still alive, all inhabiting tropical fresh waters. Three very similar forms come from Africa, one from the Amazon and Paraguay Rivers of South America, and one from Queensland, Australia.

The East London Coelacanth, *Latimeria chalumnae*, was unknown until 1938, when a fishing boat off the coast of South Africa pulled in a five-foot, blue, rough-scaled fish with strange, fleshy bases to several of its fins and a peculiar triangle-shaped tail. Although the boat crew decided to save the queer fish, they did not realize the sensational nature of their unique catch.

As it turned out, the fish belonged to a group supposed to have become extinct sixty to seventy million years ago—about the same time that the dinosaurs disappeared from the earth. Moreover, this ancient group of fishes originated about 400 million years ago and is the one that includes the ancestors of all land vertebrates (backboned animals).

Through an unfortunate series of circumstances all of the internal soft parts and much of the skeleton of the East London coelacanth were discarded before it was examined by any expert. Therefore, strangely enough, the anatomy of some of its fossil relatives is better known. As a result of the first catch in 1938, an intense search was started for more specimens, in the hope that we might learn more about this "living fossil". In late 1952 fishermen took another coelacanth, and Professor J. L. B. Smith, leading South African ichthyologist, was rushed by plane to the scene of the find. He succeeded in preserving

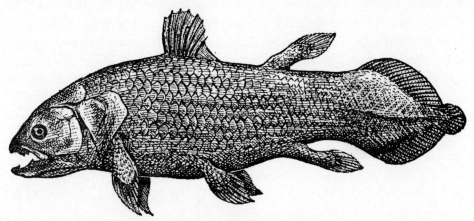

RETURNED FROM THE PAST

The East London coelacanth belongs to a group of fishes that was supposed to have become extinct from sixty to seventy million years ago. In 1938, a fishing boat off the coast of South Africa pulled in a five-foot, rough-scaled specimen. Late in 1952, a native fisherman caught another coelacanth of a different species in the same general region. Both finds caused a great stir in the scientific world.

the specimen, to the delight of the scientific world. Most surprising of all, the fish turned out to be a different species. Scientists are now wondering more than ever what rarities still remain undiscovered in the depths of the sea.

The African Lungfish, *Protopterus annectens*, has been known to live longer without food and water than any other backboned animal. Specimens have been kept alive in a natural state of suspended animation in blocks of hardened mud for more than four years, after which they were "awakened" successfully to take up a more ordinary life for a fish.

When the waters of its native tropical streams, lakes, and swamps commence to dry up during times of unusual drought or during regular annual dry seasons, the lungfish sinks into the mud. Being an air-breather, it is little inconvenienced so long as the mud remains quite soft; but when it begins to harden, the fish has to struggle to the surface to obtain a gulp of air. Nevertheless, the lungfish continues to force its way upward periodically, until at last the surface has become quite hard, and all that remains to indicate the fish's presence is a breathing hole scarcely larger in diameter than a lead pencil.

Underneath in the still pliable mud, the lungfish now prepares itself for its summer rest, or "estivation" as it is called. It folds its tail over its head, coming to rest in a tight U-shaped position, head and tail uppermost. Its skin secretes a thin covering, protecting all but the mouth of the fish against undue drying out. The mud gradually hardens all around it, and finally it is completely encased as if in stone. Profound changes in the working of the body parts of the immobile

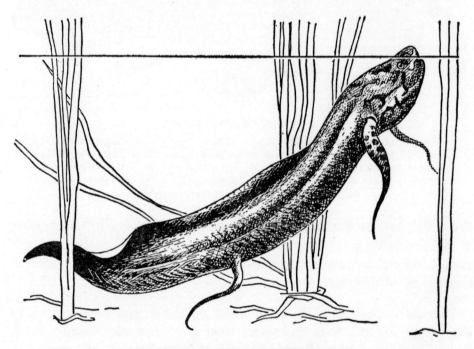

THIS ONE "SLEEPS" AND BREATHES AIR

The African lungfish provides us with a remarkable example of an animal that can live for a long period of time in a natural state of suspended animation. Some lungfish have existed in blocks of hardened mud for more than four years, and have afterwards resumed their usual life. Normally, lungfish must come to the surface for air, or drown.

lungfish take place, enabling it to live at a very slow rate, so to speak, and to withstand the accumulation of waste products in its blood. When the rains return and soften the hardened mud, the fish is

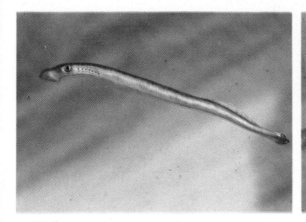

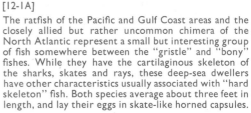

[12-1]

Fish were the first backboned animals to develop. Their fossil records, dating back some 400 million years, indicate that the ancient innovators have been extinct for at least 280 million years but have a close, living relative in the lamprey. Lampreys are eel-shaped, scaleless, jawless fish with a single nostril and a rough, rasping tongue with which they scrape away an entrance into the body cavity of other fish for the attachment of the circular, sucking mouth.   *See page 1404*

[12-1A]

The ratfish of the Pacific and Gulf Coast areas and the closely allied but rather uncommon chimera of the North Atlantic represent a small but interesting group of fish somewhere between the "gristle" and "bony" fishes. While they have the cartilaginous skeleton of the sharks, skates and rays, these deep-sea dwellers have other characteristics usually associated with "hard skeleton" fish. Both species average about three feet in length, and lay their eggs in skate-like horned capsules.

Rays vary in size from less than a foot in width to the giant devil ray, or manta, with a "wing-spread" of twenty feet weighing more than a ton. For the most part they live at the bottom of the sea where their speckled dorsal side blends with the sand and silt; the manta is a surface dweller, and a few species inhabit fresh water. Several hundred kinds of rays and the very similar looking skates are known. Rays give birth to live young and swim by flapping their expanded pectoral fins like wings, while skates lay eggs and swim with an undulating motion.   *See page 1417*

[12-B&C]

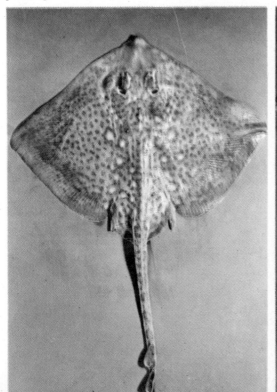
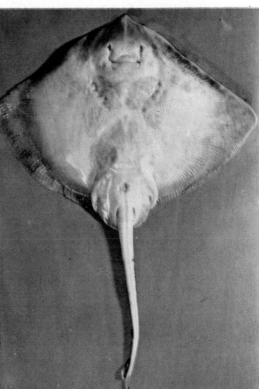

This Australian lungfish is found only in the Murray River of Queensland. Altogether five species of this freshwater, living fossil are known—three in Africa, one in the Paraguay and Amazon Rivers of South America, and the Australian variety, all ranging in size from three to six feet—but fossil remains indicate they were once widespread. Many of the internal structures of lungfish are similar to those of amphibians. The "lung" is an air bladder with a muscle structure and compartments like the lungs of higher vertebrates, and these fish must have access to air or they will drown. They usually spend the dry season encased in mud ("estivation"—the summer equivalent of hibernation) with only a small air hole to betray their presence.

See page 1420

[12-2]

[12-2A]

The bowfin, or freshwater dogfish, is the sole survivor of a group once relatively abundant in Europe and North America but now found only in the United States, from Florida to Vermont and Texas to the Great Lakes, and the neighbouring areas of Canada. Stocky-bodied, aggressive fish, they reach lengths of over two feet and weights of more than ten pounds, but they are not generally considered good game or food fish. The black spot on the tail fin is characteristic of the males. The unusual microscopic gill structure of the bowfins is thought to aid them in breathing in foul water; they also breathe air, taking gulps at the surface and passing the gas into a specialized air bladder.

See page 1430

aroused from its "sleep" and soon begins to feed voraciously, principally on other fishes and on snails and bivalves.

The lungfish has small gills, but must have access to air or it drowns. About once every twenty minutes it comes to the surface to swallow a gulp of air, passing the gas into a pair of air bladders or lungs that open into the gullet. Among the many other unusual features of structure found in the lungfish are a pair of nostrils that open from the exterior into the mouth; in this respect lungfish differ from almost all other kinds of fishes. The lungfish has a long body with long dorsal and anal fins that seem to come together in a sharp point to form the tail. The pectoral and pelvic fins are merely long, tapering ribbons. Scales are small and completely embedded in the skin. In colour it is brown or tan with black or dark brown mottling.

The male lungfish prepares a clear area among dense plant growth on the muddy bottom, and there the female lays her eggs. These are about one-eighth of an inch in diameter and are guarded by the male and kept supplied with fresh water by vigorous movements of his tail. After about eight days they hatch, and the young are also guarded for a time. Young lungfish are unusual in having external gills—four pairs of them—like those seen in a number of amphibians. As the fish mature, these organs gradually disappear. Lungfish attain a size of at least three feet. They are a popular food with native Africans.

The African lungfish is widely distributed in the fresh waters of tropical Africa. There are two other closely related African species, one of which reaches a length of at least six feet.

Sturgeons and Paddle Fishes
—Famed for Their Eggs

THE STURGEONS are famed for their eggs, which we eat as caviare. Although these fishes are dwellers in the sea for the most part, they leave salt water and go up into rivers to lay their eggs. There are some sturgeons, however, that live permanently in streams and lakes. Perhaps as many as twenty-five species exist; their cousins the paddle fishes are far fewer in number, and like the sturgeons make their home only in the Northern Hemisphere.

Although the sturgeons and the paddle fishes are not close relatives of the sharks, they remind us of them in several ways. For one thing, they have little true bone in their skeletons—mostly these are gristle. (Thus the sturgeons and paddle fishes are placed in the order Chondrostei—"gristle-boned".) Five rows of bony plates protect the bodies of some; others are almost completely naked-skinned. Scientists look upon them as primitive forms of the ray-finned group of the bony fishes.

The Atlantic Sturgeon, *Acipenser oxyrhynchus,* roots up sand or mud with its pointed, flattened snout to obtain the small, bottom-inhabiting invertebrates and fishes upon which it feeds. On the underside of its snout is a row of four barbels, or feelers, that are undoubtedly used to detect food, and behind these is the sucking mouth, which can be protruded. The rather long body has five longitudinal rows of large, bony plates, the fish's scales. The tail is sharklike, the upper lobe being much longer than the lower.

Atlantic sturgeon are found on both sides of the Atlantic from the St. Lawrence River to the Carolinas in the west, and from Scandinavia to the Black Sea in the east. During the spring they enter large rivers,

1424

and travel upstream to spawn. Large numbers used to be caught at this season for their flesh, which is especially fine when smoked, and for their eggs, which are one of the original sources of the caviare of commerce. The eggs are adhesive, heavier than water, and a little larger than one-eighth of an inch in diameter. An average female contains over one and one-half million of them.

PRODUCER OF CAVIARE

The Atlantic sturgeon is a long fish covered with a tough skin and bony plates. It uses its strange snout to burrow in the bottom for food. The average female produces in excess of one and a half million eggs; prepared and salted, these are known as caviare.

Fully grown Atlantic sturgeon are usually about seven or eight feet long, but eighteen-foot specimens are said to have been caught on both sides of the Atlantic Ocean. At present, in the United States and Canada at least, the Atlantic sturgeon is relatively rare, and is apparently becoming more scarce all the time.

The White Sturgeon, *Acipenser transmontanus,* is the largest fish found in North American waters. It is native to the coast and rivers of the north-west of the United States, and has been reported to attain a weight of eighteen to nineteen hundred pounds. One twelve-and-a-half-foot female weighed 1,285 pounds. Unfortunately, this valuable commercial fish is now very rare, and is probably dying out. Heavy fishing, pollution, and large dams that keep it from reaching its breeding grounds upstream have all taken their toll.

The Beluga, *Huso huso,* also a sturgeon, is the largest freshwater fish in the world. It is found in the Volga, Dnieper, and other European rivers, and in the Caspian and the Black Seas. A specimen of this aquatic giant, weighing 3,210 pounds, is on record, and several exceeding two thousand pounds are known. One fish of 2,250 pounds was fourteen feet, two inches long, and a 2,680-pound female contained over 320 pounds of eggs, or roe, enough to provide caviare canapés for an army.

The Paddle Fish, *Polyodon spathula,* has been called the most remarkable freshwater fish in North America because of its many bizarre and unique features. Its naked body—it has scales only on part of the tail—is quite sharklike in general appearance, but its head is entirely different from that of any other type of fish. Projecting out from the front is a long, flattened snout, about one-third to one-half as long as all the rest of the fish. Beneath this paddle-shaped projection is the wide mouth, the lower jaw of which can be dropped down to form a truly cavelike opening. The tiny eyes are located alongside the base of the paddle. The gill covers are large and soft and end toward the rear in a heavy triangular point.

The paddle fish feeds upon small aquatic creatures like freshwater shrimps, water fleas, and aquatic insects. It also eats some vegetable matter. Its paddle is undoubtedly used to detect the presence of food, for it is well provided with nerves and sense organs, and is swung from side to side in an exploratory fashion while the fish swims. When it encounters any tiny creatures, the fish opens its mouth wide and literally swims over its food, the water passing out through the gill-chambers, while small objects are retained by the gill rakers which act like a sieve.

The reproductive habits of paddle fish are still a mystery despite the efforts of numerous scientists to find out how, when, and where they lay their eggs. The smallest paddle fish ever caught was about five-eighths of an inch long and at this size did not yet have a paddle. It is believed that the fish spawns in the main channels of large rivers in the Mississippi system. Sexual maturity is reached when the fish is between thirty-nine and fifty-five inches in length. Maximum length exceeds six feet and maximum weight 150 pounds. The flesh of the paddle fish is usually smoked, and the eggs are used as caviare.

THE MOST REMARKABLE NORTH AMERICAN FISH

An odd creature indeed is the paddle fish—it looks rather like a shark in some respects, but its head is quite unlike that of other fish. It possesses a long, flattened snout, shaped somewhat like a paddle, which is used for detecting food, and under this is a wide mouth. The tiny eyes are located at the base of the paddle. Except for a part of its tail, this fish is without scales.

Only two species of paddle fish exist today—one in the rivers of China, the other in the United States.

Gars and Bowfins—Freshwater Savages

THE GARS and the bowfins are rugged-looking fishes, extremely fierce and voracious in their habits. Because of the havoc they wreak among other living things and because their flesh is ill-tasting, they are most unpopular with fishermen. Conservationists point out, however, that these predatory fishes frequently keep the hordes of suckers, catfish, and minnows in check, and thus help to maintain the balance of nature.

Although today not many members of this group exist—we know of only ten species of gars and one of the bowfins—in the remote past they were far more numerous. Some of these ancestors lived in Europe, but today we do not find the bowfin outside the fresh waters of the United States and Canada, and the gars live only in North and Central America and Cuba. Sometimes, however, they stray into brackish and salt water. They make up the order Protospondyli.

The Longnose Gar, *Lepisosteus osseus*, with its long, beaklike jaws bearing strong, conical teeth throughout their length, is a prime example of a fish that preys on other fishes. Stealthily it glides alongside a prospective victim and with a sudden swift, sideward snap, securely impales the fish on its needle-sharp teeth. Usually the prey is caught crosswise, but it is eventually juggled around so that its head points toward the gar's mouth and is then swallowed whole. Feeding is often done at night. In many places gars are considered a serious menace to food, game, and forage fishes, but this has been proved true in only a limited number of cases.

On the other hand, longnose gars themselves seem well protected against their enemies, by the heavy diamond-shaped scales that cover their body like a coat of mail. So hard they can turn the sharpest knife, these scales are of a type commonly found on ancient fishes, but absent

1428

among the more recently evolved, streamlined, fast-swimming species and their descendants. Although the gar's scales are jointed with one another, they do not make a very flexible covering, and this may be one reason why gars are sluggish creatures, rarely moving rapidly except while feeding. The body of the longnose gar is round and long. The dorsal and anal fins are located just in front of the tail.

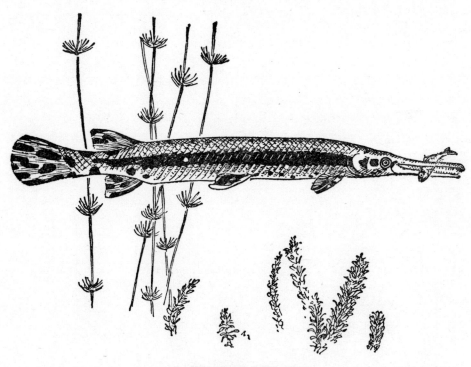

A FISH THAT EATS FISH

The longnose gar has a taste for fish, and its long, beaklike jaws and strong, conical teeth are excellent equipment for catching them. The gar swims quietly beside its prospective prey, then suddenly snaps its jaws to the side, impaling the victim on its sharp teeth. In general, the gar is a slow-moving creature.

Periodically, as the water in which they live becomes foul or too warm, gars rise to the surface and take a gulp of air. They spawn in shallow water, usually among weeds, during the spring. The numerous eggs are adhesive; a fifty-six-inch female, weighing thirty-two pounds, contained 77,150 of them. A maximum length of five feet is attained. Longnose gars are widely distributed from Quebec and Vermont to Florida, and from the Great Lakes, excepting Lake Superior, to northern Mexico.

The Alligator Gar, *Lepisosteus spatula*, from the lower Mississippi valley and other streams draining the Gulf Coast, is the second largest freshwater fish in North America. There are authentic records of specimens more than nine feet long and unconfirmed ones of twelve and fourteen feet. One female that was nine feet, eight and one-half inches in length, weighed 302 pounds.

The Bowfin, *Amia calva*, represents the last living survivor of a group of fishes that was relatively abundant in the geological past in Europe and North America. Now found only in fresh waters from Vermont to Florida and the Great Lakes to Texas, the bowfin holds its own very well with numerous fishes of more recent origin. In fact, it is often considered a scourge of such "modern" gamefishes as bass and perch, just as are those other "living fossils", the gars.

Bowfins feed on fishes of all sorts and on crayfish and molluscs as well. Their strong, sharp-toothed jaws enable them to attack quite large fish. Even small birds sometimes fall victims to their voracious

A FISH THAT SOMETIMES EATS BIRDS

With its sturdy jaws and powerful teeth, the bowfin, an American freshwater fish, will attack other big fish and even some birds. The male is remarkably "domestic"—not only does he make a sort of nest for his mate, but he also protects the eggs and the young that emerge from them.

appetites. Although they fight hard when hooked, they have never found favour with sportsmen. Nor are they considered a desirable food, except in a few scattered localities. They reach lengths of over two feet and weights of more than ten pounds, females being larger than males.

The stocky body of the bowfin is round in cross-section and covered with dark olive scales, shading to lighter underneath. During the breeding season, the pectoral, pelvic, and anal fins of the males become bright green. Males also show a large black spot at the upper base of the tail fin.

The male bowfin prepares a nest in late spring by clearing a space among the plants and making a small depression in the bottom, where the female lays large numbers of eggs, between one-sixteenth and one-eighth of an inch in diameter. These are adhesive and become attached to plants and rootlets within and surrounding the nest. The male guards the eggs until they hatch, that is, from four to fourteen days, depending on the temperature. For the first few days, the newly hatched fish attach themselves by means of a sucking disc to the plants or bottom. After that they become free-swimming, and are herded about in a school by the male, who still bravely protects them for a month or more, sometimes until they are three or four inches long.

Bowfins have gills of unusual microscopic structure that are thought to aid them in breathing when in foul waters. They also can breathe air by taking a gulp at the surface and passing the gas into the specialized air bladder.

Important Fishes—Herring, Salmon, Pike, and Their Relatives

ECONOMICALLY, this is our most valuable group of fishes—it provides us with about twenty million tons of commercial fish each year. In this tremendous assemblage we find all the herring-like forms, the salmons and the trouts and their relatives, the pike and pickerels, and a host of other species. They inhabit both fresh and salt waters of all the oceans and the continents, from the Arctic and the Antarctic to the Equator, and from the depths of the sea to high mountain streams.

The two families most important to our commerce are the herring, shad, and sardines (Clupeidae) and the salmon and trout (Salmonidae). In fact, the herrings and their relatives rank first in economic importance among all the families of fishes. They occur in all seas, and include more than 150 different species. Some of them enter fresh water, frequently to spawn. A few live only in fresh water, but the majority never leave the sea.

The salmon and trout were originally found only in the fresh and salt waters of the Northern Hemisphere, none naturally dwelling farther south than California, Georgia, Spain, the Caspian Sea, and the Kamchatka Peninsula. Man, however, has introduced them into suitable waters over much of the world. They either live their entire life in fresh water or spend part of it in the sea, returning to fresh water to spawn. As many as one hundred species have been listed, but the actual number is considerably less than this.

The pike, the muskellunge, and the three species of pickerels (family Esocidae) are all native to the fresh waters of North America, with the pike also found in Europe and Asia. There are three or four species of American mudminnows and a single European one; they are freshwater forms and are generally classified as a single family (Umbridae).

Among the other well-known fishes—and here we are mustering only a few names from the great finny legions of this order—are the tarpons and ten-pounders, the bonefish, the pirarucu, the milkfish, the whitefishes and ciscos, the grayling, the smelt, and the Alaska blackfish.

Although many of these fishes are highly specialized and of relatively recent evolution, the group (order Isospondyli, a name meaning "equal vertebrae") as a whole is not advanced, and contains some of the most primitive of bony fishes. We identify its members by the lack of spines in the fins and by the fact that the pelvic fins (if the fishes have them), are located toward the rear of the body.

Scientists identify these fishes mostly by the structure of the skull and upper jaw.

The Tarpon, *Tarpon atlanticus*, has become a famous gamefish because of its fighting qualities and leaping powers. Since its flesh is often coarse and bitter, it is seldom eaten and therefore is not of commercial importance as a foodfish. The largest tarpon ever caught by means of tackle weighed 247 pounds and was almost seven and one-half feet long. It is known, however, that the tarpon sometimes reaches weights of three hundred pounds and can grow to a length of nearly eight feet.

Tarpon are handsome, silvery fish with large shiny scales, a prominent mouth, and a long fine extension of the rear portion of the dorsal fin. They are inhabitants of the tropical Atlantic Ocean, normally not far from shore. They are frequently found in brackish waters, far up tropical rivers, and in lakes. Evidently tarpon can live for years in fresh water. They usually range from Florida and the Gulf Coast to Brazil, but straggle as far north as Nova Scotia. They frequent the west coast of Africa and are common in the West Indies, but rare in Bermuda.

Very few data were available on the tarpon's life history until the New York Aquarium, in 1938, established a laboratory on the west coast of Florida, in the heart of tarpon country, to study this fish. We now know that tarpon mature when about seven years old and four feet long, and that their numerous eggs are undoubtedly laid in open waters and sink to the bottom, and that very young tarpon go through a number of different stages before they assume a typical tarpon-like appearance. It was also discovered that the characteristic habit of "rolling" in which tarpon break the water surface, is for the purpose of obtaining atmospheric air, which is stored in the fish's air bladder. Despite their large, well-developed gills, tarpon die if denied access to the surface even though kept in pure, rapidly flowing sea water.

A FIGHTER AND A HIGH JUMPER

Although it is too bitter to make good eating, the tarpon is famed as a gamefish. It may grow to nearly eight feet in length, and weigh as much as three hundred pounds. Fishermen esteem it because it puts up a good fight, often leaping surprisingly high.

A smaller species of tarpon lives in the Indian Ocean and western Pacific. It, too, often enters rivers and remains for considerable lengths of time in fresh water.

The Bonefish, *Albula vulpes,* grows by shrinking! For some time during its early development this fish looks entirely different from the adult, being transparent, long, and very compressed, that is, extremely thin from side to side. At this stage it is called a "leptocephalus larva". After reaching a length of about three and one-half inches, it begins a remarkable transformation. The fish actually shrinks in size—as much as three-quarters of an inch in four days. Meanwhile, its ribbon-like body gradually takes on the cylindrical, tapering shape of the adult bonefish and also acquires some of the silver colouring for which the species is famous. Its fins move into their final positions, and its head assumes the usual bonefish shape, with a characteristic piglike snout overhanging the small mouth. During this process of growth the fish shrinks to less than one-third of its former length.

After taking on the typical form of an adult, the young one-inch bonefish begins to grow in the usual fashion. It generally reaches a weight between two and five pounds, but can grow much larger. The record bonefish ever caught with fishing tackle weighed sixteen pounds and was thirty-eight inches long. Like its distant relative, the tarpon, the bonefish is a great fighter when hooked and is highly esteemed as a gamefish.

Although adult bonefish travel in small groups or are solitary, the young are often found in sizable schools. They frequently come in with the tide to feed on mudflats. Burying their snouts in the soft bottom, they search for molluscs and crustaceans which they crush with their blunt teeth. Sometimes the water is so shallow that their silvery tails project above the surface as they grub for food. Adults also feed in this manner.

Bonefish have been found in tropical seas and inlets throughout the world. On the Atlantic coast of North America they occur as far north as Cape Cod, but are not numerous north of Florida. On the Pacific coast they have been taken as far north as Monterey, but seem to be nowhere common.

The Atlantic Herring, *Clupea harengus,* is one of the most numerous of all the backboned animals on earth. A single gigantic school, or shoal, may contain three billion individuals, and there are undoubtedly scores of such shoals in the North Atlantic. They are easily captured in great numbers with nets and are perhaps the most important single foodfish in the world. About three and one-quarter billion pounds are caught annually—to be consumed fresh, salted (pickled herring), salted-and-smoked (kippered and red herring), and canned.

Herring are quite beautiful with their silvery, iridescent sides and deep steel-blue backs. They grow to be about seventeen inches long and may live for twenty years. This is very rare, however, for, before they reach an age of ten years, the vast majority of herring are eaten by the innumerable animals that prey upon them, including other fishes, squid, whales, and man.

The food of the herring consists of the small, floating animals that abound in northern seas. Sometimes they feed by simply swimming open-mouthed through masses of these creatures, straining them out with their gill-rakers, which are numerous, dense, bristle-like projections in the region of the gills, that act like sieves. All water entering the mouth and eventually passing over the gills must pass through the gill rakers, leaving behind all but the finest particles. At other times herring chase somewhat larger prey, snapping up such creatures one at a time.

Herring gather into large shoals, more or less inshore, to spawn at almost any time of the year, depending on the particular locality and race of fish involved. Astronomical numbers of eggs are laid, for each female produces about thirty thousand. The eggs are heavier than sea water, and adhesive, sinking and sticking to whatever plants, stones, or bottom they happen to touch. Hatching takes place from ten to forty days later, depending on the temperature; the colder the water, the slower the development of the fish in the egg.

The Pacific Herring, *Clupea pallasi*, is not as economically important as the Atlantic herring. Somewhat more than one billion pounds are caught each year. Its habits are similar to those of the Atlantic species. It spawns in large groups, mostly on kelp beds and among eel grass, from midwinter to June, depending on the latitude. The heavy, sticky eggs hatch in one to three weeks.

The American Shad, *Alosa sapidissima*, was once much more abundant than it is today. Its life cycle, like the salmon's, makes it especially vulnerable to human mismanagement. Each year, from January to July according to the latitude, adult shad leave the sea, where they have been feeding on small ocean creatures, and run up the rivers of the United States' Atlantic coast to spawn. The males or buck shad weigh from one and one-half to six pounds, while the females or roe shad weigh from three and one-half to eight and, rarely, up to twelve pounds. They select shallow water over pebbly or sandy areas for reproduction.

The average female deposits about thirty thousand pale pink or amber eggs which neither float nor sink, but rest lightly on the bottom. They hatch in six to ten days. The young shad remain in fresh water until the autumn, when they move into brackish and, later, salt water. Their parents return to the sea very soon after egg laying.

While travelling up rivers and streams, shad used to be caught with great nets almost a mile long that sometimes stretched from shore to shore. So many were caught that they were used as fertilizer. In this way whole "runs" were undoubtedly destroyed. The pollution of rivers and the erection of dams, destroying the breeding places of the shad or preventing the adults from reaching them, are two other ways in which man has thoughtlessly destroyed this delicious and valuable natural food resource, and is continuing to destroy it.

In 1871 the shad was introduced into the Pacific coastal waters of the United States, where it has now become fairly well established from Southern California to Alaska.

The Pilchard, *Sardina pilchardus*, when young is called the sardine and is the object of an important fishery in France, Portugal, and Spain. As adults, too, when they are approximately seven inches long, pilchards are fished commercially. They inhabit most of the Mediterranean Sea and the waters off the western coast of Europe from North Africa to the British Isles. They migrate along the coast and are found farther north during the summer and autumn.

Pilchards look somewhat like herring, to which they are quite closely related. They lay their floating eggs offshore, the time of the year depending on the temperature of the water. This means that the farther south that the fish are, the earlier in the year they spawn.

The name "sardine" is derived, we believe, from the island of Sardinia, and goes back to antiquity.

The California Sardine, *Sardinops caerulea*, supports one of the largest fisheries in the United States. During the 1936-37 fishing season well over one and one-half billion pounds of California sardines were taken by the United States and Canada and either canned or "reduced", the latter being the process of making oil and meal out of the fish. In addition, many hundreds of thousands of pounds were used as bait —in fishing for tuna, for example.

Since that season, however, there has been an alarming decrease in the weight of sardines caught, for any given amount of fishing effort. To find the cause of the reduced catch and prevent permanent damage to the industry, an extensive programme of scientific investigation has been set up. The object is to find out anything about the California sardine that might have a bearing on its response to heavy, continuous fishing. In effect, this means that practically everything about the sardine's life history and its relation to its surroundings must be determined. Consequently, fishery experts are now learning many facts about the California sardine—things that ought to be known about all economically important fish and which, unfortunately, are known about very few.

California sardines first spawn when they are two, three, or four years old and from a little more than seven to a little less than ten inches long. Spawning takes place from late winter to early summer, principally fifty to two hundred miles off the coast of southern California. Each female lays about one hundred thousand eggs. These float about on the surface for two or three days, when hatching takes place. Adult sardines are rovers, and it is believed that this tendency soon shows itself in the young. At any rate, schools of sardines, great and small, make extensive and complicated migrations that investigators are only beginning to understand. In their travels, these fish range all the way from south-eastern Alaska to the southern tip of Baja California, but they apparently spend more time in California waters than anywhere else.

Like its relative the pilchard, the California sardine feeds on minute floating plants and animals, which it strains out of the sea by means of a sievelike structure near the gills.

The Menhaden, *Brevoortia tyrannus*, is today the basis of the largest single fishery in the United States. Between 800 and 900 million pounds are taken off the Atlantic and Gulf coasts each year, mostly by special boats equipped with purse seines (long, flat nets with a drawstring to close the bottom after a shoal of fish is encircled). This means that well over a billion menhaden are captured each year.

This great fishery provides very little food for man, although the roe of the menhaden is very similar to that of the American shad, and a few have been canned. By far the greatest part of the catch is "reduced", that is, converted into fish meal (used in hog, cattle, and poultry feeds), oil (used in soaps, paints, insecticides, and in many other industries), and fertilizer. In all, there are five different species of menhaden, but this species is the one most common off the northeastern coast.

Menhaden feed principally on the myriads of microscopic plants found floating near the surface of the sea, which they filter out of the water with their fine, sieve-like gill apparatus. They swim through the water with open mouths, and it has been estimated that as much as seven gallons pass into their mouths and out past their gills each

[12-3]

The gars, like the bowfin, are remnants of an ancient family, some 10 species inhabiting the freshwater lakes and rivers of North and Central America and Cuba. They sometimes stray into brackish and salt water bays although the short-nose gar is less commonly found in such areas than the other species. The beak-like jaws of the more slender longnose gar are equipped with strong conical teeth throughout their length, giving at least one member of a particularly savage family an extraordinarily effective weapon. Gars have a defensive weapon equally effective in preserving their species—their milt and roe are poisonous.   *See page 1428*

[12-3B]

Rainbow trout originally occurred only on the West Coast of the United States from southern California to south-eastern Alaska, but because these fish respond so well to all phases of artificial culture, man has been able to introduce them into suitable lakes and streams the world over. The sea-going variety, known as "steel-heads", return to fresh water to spawn. The usual adult rainbow weighs from two to eight pounds, although a giant of fifty-two and a half pounds has been reported.
See page 1443

[12-3A]

The life cycle of the American shad, like the salmon's, makes this aristocrat of the herring family especially vulnerable to human mismanagement. From January to July, according to the latitude, the adult sea-dwelling shad move up the rivers of the North Atlantic Coast to spawn in fresh water. At times whole "runs" have been destroyed, so many of the delicious and valuable fish having been caught they were used as fertilizer. Introduced into Pacific Coast waters almost 100 years ago, shad have become fairly well established from southern California to Alaska.
See page 1436

[12-3C]

Brook trout are native to eastern North America but, like the rainbow, have been introduced successfully into other parts of this continent, Europe, Argentina and New Zealand. They vary greatly in size, depending mostly on the supply of suitable food. Where the diet is composed mainly of insects, brook trout rarely exceed nine inches in length; larger individuals feed on other fish, crayfish, frogs and salamanders, as well as insects.   *See page 1446*

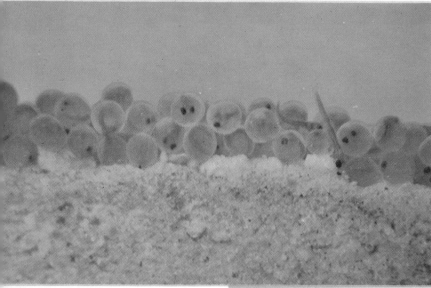

The "eyed egg" stage of the brown trout. When first laid, the slightly adhesive eggs of the brown trout are spherical and a little less than one-fifth of an inch in diameter. Like the eggs of all trout and salmon, they are a little heavier than water, and the female deposits them in a nest ("redd") placed in relation to the current so that an eddy is formed and the water directly over the eggs actually moves upstream.

See page 1446

[12-4]

[12-4A]

From 40 to 70 days after the eggs are laid the fry hatch, with no particular resemblance to their parents. There are salt-water varieties of the brown trout—so differently coloured from the others that they were once thought to be a different species—but both kinds spawn only in swift-running fresh water. While the rate of growth slows down as fish mature, all species continue growing as long as they live.

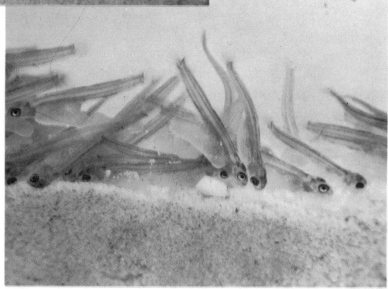

[12-4B]

The brown trout can live in warmer waters than other members of the family. It occurs naturally in Europe from Iceland and Norway to the Mediterranean; in Corsica, Sardinia and Algeria, and in Asia east to the Himalayas. While not considered as fine a gamefish as other trout it, too, has been transplanted to all parts of the world. Brown and brook trout have been crossed in fish hatcheries, and while the hybrids are hardy, handsome fish, they are apparently completely sterile.

[12-5]

The chum, or dog salmon, occurs north of the Sacramento River and Puget Sound. It averages about 18 inches in length and may weigh anywhere from 10 to 20 pounds. As it spawns nearer the mouth of the rivers, the chum has not been so adversely affected by huge power dams as have other species. Salmon spawn during the autumn, most often on gravelly shallows. The female digs the redd by lying on her side and rapidly vibrating her tail to create currents which displace stones, gravel and sand on the bottom. The male will defend the site against other fish.   *See pages 1440, 1446*

[12-5A]

The three species of pickerel are native to North America and, in general, are the smaller members of the somewhat exclusive family of long, slender gamefish which includes the pike and muskellunge. The chain pickerel may run as large as a good-sized pike—up to four feet—and hybrids between this pickerel, pike and muskellunge are often found in nature. Reproduction in many species of fish is a very casual affair: the female releases the eggs and the male the sperm without any contact, fertilization being a matter of proximity and chance.

See page 1453

[12-6]

Pike are found throughout the Northern Hemisphere—Europe, Asia and North America playing host to considerable numbers of this excellent gamefish. Pike prefer quiet waters which offer weedy lairs where they can lie in wait for prey; when some unsuspecting fish swims by, they dash out with split-second speed to snap it up. Occasionally pike will stalk their prey, the stealthy approach being followed by the same death-dealing sprint. Record weights for pike are a little over 50 pounds.

See page 1452

[12-6A]

Pike have insatiable appetites and consume enormous quantities of food in the course of a year. While small specimens feed on worms, crustaceans and insect larvae, large adult pike have been known to eat birds and even mammals. They are principally fish-eaters. Teeth that are broken off or worn down are replaced, but the fish does not shed the entire set each summer as legend would have it.

See page 1452

minute. The average length of the menhaden is about one foot and they seldom exceed fifteen inches. They lay floating eggs. In the vicinity of New York, the peak of the spawning season is in May and June.

The European Anchovy, *Engraulis encrasicholus*, is best known to Americans as a canned delicacy—after its tender, oily flesh has been processed into fillets or into paste. It is a common fish in the Mediterranean Sea and on the western coast of Europe from North Africa to Norway, where it migrates, with the change of season, in large schools. It spawns during the spring and summer, laying floating eggs that hatch in a few days. Like the eggs of most anchovies, these are ellipsoidal (longer than wide or thick) in shape. The vast majority of floating fish eggs are spherical, but no one has yet advanced any reason why anchovy eggs should not conform to the general rule.

The various anchovies are small, flesh-eating fishes that, as a rule, live in schools, more or less near shore in temperate and tropical seas over most of the world. They somewhat resemble herring in their body shape and silvery colour but differ in having a short snout in front of large eyes, and a receding lower jaw that seems to fit inside the upper one, giving the fish a peculiar "chinless" look. In South America especially, anchovies ascend streams, and some may live permanently in fresh water.

Nearly ninety New World species have been described; there are undoubtedly quite a number that live in the Old World. Of the several American anchovies only the Pacific Anchovy, *Engraulis mordax*, is utilized to any extent for food, and the greater part of the catch of this species is used as bait rather than for human consumption. The Pacific anchovy ranges from Baja California to British Columbia. It grows to a length of about seven inches.

The Milkfish, *Chanos chanos*, is prized for food through much of the Orient, where it is the most valuable of all the fishes cultivated in ponds, being especially important in Java and the Philippines. Although it is normally found only in salt or brackish water, it does very well in fresh, and can be reared in both salt and freshwater ponds. At certain seasons of the year, tremendous numbers of milkfish fry appear along the coast. They are scooped out and planted in ponds, where they put on size rapidly, growing as much as twenty inches within one year.

EAL / 12—D

Little or nothing is known about the spawning habits of milkfish, for they never reproduce in captivity. This does not limit the usefulness of the fish, however, since there is always an abundant supply of fresh stock to be obtained from nature. Milkfish are quite widely distributed in shallow water from the Red Sea and east coast of Africa, through the Indian Ocean and East Indies, to southern Japan, New South Wales, Hawaii, and the Pacific coast of Mexico.

The milkfish has a slender body with a small head and a large, widely forked tail. It is coloured a brilliant, metallic, silvery blue or green above, silver along its sides, and white below. It has no teeth and feeds on tiny plants and animals which it strains out of the water with a special accessory gill apparatus. A swift, powerful swimmer, the milkfish can leap more than twenty feet in the air. Adults range from about twenty-eight to sixty inches in length.

The Pirarucu, *Arapaima gigas*, is the most important foodfish of the Amazon River. It is usually speared or harpooned and its flesh cut into thin slabs to be dried in the sun. It is probably the largest fresh-water fish in South America, but authorities disagree on the maximum size it may attain, some claiming fifteen feet and four hundred pounds, others twelve feet and three hundred pounds, and still others only seven feet. Undoubtedly the first of these estimates is too generous; no recently caught example has exceeded eight feet. Today the largest specimens fished are seldom more than five feet long or weigh more than 175 pounds.

The pirarucu has a shape all of its own. It has a somewhat cylindrical body and a rather small, flattened head. The mouth, however, is quite large. Dorsal and anal fins are located far to the rear, almost surrounding the small rounded tail fin. The body is covered with very large scales, coloured olive green toward the front of the fish and gradually becoming more and more tinged with scarlet toward the rear, until they are quite red near the tail.

The range of the pirarucu includes much of the Amazon Basin and British Guiana. The fish is an air-breather and drowns if kept under water. It constructs a nest and cares for its eggs and young. Because of a shortage of these valuable fish, the Brazilian government has undertaken experiments in growing the pirarucu in ponds.

The Atlantic Salmon, *Salmo salar*, probably has been studied more than any other fish, but there are still many things not understood about it. For example, no one can yet explain how salmon manage to return to the same river, even the identical tributary, in which they were hatched—after spending years out in the trackless ocean. That they do this has been demonstrated by tagging or otherwise marking young fish and then catching them again years later, in the same stream. Occasionally "stray" salmon turn up in other river systems, but they usually go back to their so-called "parent stream" to spawn. This behaviour is not inherited, for, if salmon still within the eggs are transplanted from one stream to another, they will in later life return to the river in which they were hatched, not to the one in which their parents lived. Just what "landmarks" enable the fish to "recognize" any particular stream are still a mystery, as well as how the fish can "remember" them for several years.

The migrations of the Atlantic salmon are sometimes very extensive. While in the sea, they may travel as far as fifteen hundred miles to feeding grounds, and their journey upstream may be several hundred miles long, as in the River Rhine. During sea migrations, their sustained rate of speed has been calculated to be as high as forty-five or even sixty miles a day. Many Atlantic salmon migrations are relatively short, however, including most of those made on the Atlantic coast of North America. In some places the fish spends its whole life in fresh water, migrating from lakes into streams. These Atlantic salmon are called "landlocked".

The age at which the Atlantic salmon returns to spawn varies from one to five years. The largest individuals weigh about twenty pounds, although there are some records of rare fish that tip the scales at eighty pounds or more. As the fish become ripe (sexually mature), they lose their sleek, steel-blue and silvery colours and become a dull, reddish brown. The males often develop grotesque, hooked jaws, so distorted that they cannot completely close their mouths. The reason for these changes is unknown. As a rule, salmon do not feed once they have entered fresh water. This may mean going practically a whole year without food in those instances where a very long river trip is involved. Occasionally they will eat, however, and will strike at fishermen's flies.

Upon reaching the spawning area, the female Atlantic salmon begins to construct her nest or redd. She lies on her side, strongly arches her back and with her tail beats the gravelly bottom. This, together with the rather strong current, causes small stones, gravel, and sand to rise off the bottom and be carried some distance downstream. Over and over again the female beats the stream bottom, at intervals testing the depression she has made by sinking into it with extended anal fin. As the redd becomes deeper, the male begins to court the female by entering it with her. He has won this right by driving off other males and may have to continue doing so throughout the spawning. Digging the redd sometimes takes several days, but at last, when it is from six to twelve inches deep, the female signifies that she is ready to spawn, the male immediately comes to her side, and the eggs are laid and fertilized. After laying a batch of eggs, the female quickly moves upstream a foot or two and once more lying on her side, stirs up the bottom so vigorously with her tail that the eggs are covered by displaced gravel in less than a minute. Now the female is ready to complete another section of her redd to hold the next batch of eggs. Thus she may progressively move upstream until finally all her eggs have been laid.

Is it any wonder that many Atlantic salmon do not survive this arduous business of perpetuating the race? Few live to spawn a second time, and those that do almost invariably spawn in streams in which the journey from the sea is not very long. An Atlantic salmon that has spawned four times is extraordinary. Such a fish would be at least twelve years old, having spent two or three years in the sea between each spawning migration. Landlocked Atlantic salmon apparently survive spawning more often than do those coming from the sea.

On the north-eastern coast of North America, Atlantic salmon spawn in the autumn. The eggs do not hatch until five or six months later, that is, until April or early May. Young salmon may live for three years in fresh water before going to sea; in some places they may stay in streams for five or six years. After reaching the ocean, they grow very rapidly on the fish and shellfish they find there. At this time they lay down stores of fat that will enable them to dispense with eating during spawning and the migration associated with it.

The Atlantic salmon is native to the coast of Europe from the northern part of Norway to the northern part of Spain and as far east as the Caspian Sea. On western Atlantic shores it once existed from Delaware northward. It has been exterminated, however, in all the streams of the United States except a very few in Maine. Although salmon have been reported able to negotiate natural barriers eighteen feet high, man-made dams, locks, and other obstructions, together with pollution and the destruction of suitable spawning beds, have proved too much for this magnificent fish.

The Rainbow Trout, *Salmo gairdneri,* has confused scientists and laymen alike for many years. The problem has been: "When is a rainbow not a rainbow?" The principal controversy concerned the trout known as "steelhead". These resemble rainbow trout, but are coloured quite differently, being silvery with a bluish head and back, instead of greenish with a reddish gill cover and lateral stripe. It is now generally agreed that steelhead trout are merely sea-going rainbows, or, to put it another way, that rainbow trout are "landlocked" steelheads. In a few places, however, rainbow trout have been found to assume the steelhead coloration while remaining in fresh water. But there are several other types of rainbow-like fish whose status is still in doubt. Some ichthyologists hold that the Shasta trout, the Kamloops trout, the Kern River trout and others are all separate species. They are believed to be only geographical varieties, that is, subspecies, by other scientists, and a few of them are considered by certain experts to be not different enough to require a special name. At any rate, it is agreed that all of them are closely related to one another.

These trouts originally occurred only on the West Coast of the United States, from southern California to south-eastern Alaska. Rainbows now exist all over the world, however, having been widely introduced into suitable lakes and streams where sportsmen have wanted to fish for this sporting species. They are at present found throughout the northern United States and Canada, and they have been successfully transplanted to Europe and the British Isles, Argentina, Chile, Venezuela, South Africa, East Africa, Madagascar, Mauritius, India, Ceylon, Australia, New Zealand, Tasmania, Hawaii, and Panama. One of the reasons why rainbow trout have been established in so many faraway lands is that their eggs can be transported long distances. If kept cold, moist and free from jarring, they will stay alive for many weeks, developing so slowly that there is ample time to make long trips with them before they hatch. For example, rainbows were first introduced into New Zealand through a shipment of eggs from California in 1877—long before air express.

In fact, rainbow trout respond well to all phases of artificial culture. The eggs are gathered by "stripping", a process in which the ripe females are carefully taken out of the water and freed of their eggs by gentle pressure. The eggs are then fertilized with milt (the product of the male reproductive glands) collected from ripe males. They are allowed to develop in carefully watched trays bathed in cold running water. Females have been kept captive for as long as fourteen years, being stripped on ten to twelve occasions during this time.

Some rainbow trout remain in fresh water all their lives—even when they have access to the ocean. Others enter the sea when a year or more old, taking on the steelhead coloration. They return to their "parent stream" for spawning at an age of three to six years. Spawning occurs in winter or early spring, but steelheads enter streams at almost any time of the year, sometimes apparently only to feed. Like the Atlantic salmon they may spawn more than once. Rainbows also construct their redds and lay their eggs in almost exactly the same way as do Atlantic salmon.

The usual adult rainbow trout weighs from two to eight pounds, but thirty-six- to fifty-two-and-one-half-pound giants have been reported.

The Cutthroat Trout, *Salmo clarki*, gets its name from the slash of bright red that it has underneath its lower jaw. It was once more widely distributed through the American Far West than it is today. Each of the main river systems from Alaska to California seemed to have its own particular kind of cutthroat. This trout has now been replaced by transplanted species in many places or destroyed by pollution and other disturbances of its natural waters. When rainbow trout are introduced into cutthroat streams, the two species hybridize, but their offspring are either completely sterile or nearly so.

Those cutthroat trout that live on the western coast of North America often enter the sea when two or three years old, remaining there for a year or more before returning to fresh water to spawn. Some coastal, and all inland fish of course, spend their whole lives in fresh water. Coastal fish tend to spawn in the winter and very early spring. Those farther inland spawn in spring or summer.

The record sized cutthroat trout weighed forty-one pounds and was thirty-seven inches long. In some places, however, mature cutthroats rarely exceed a single pound.

The Brown Trout, *Salmo trutta*, can live in warmer waters than other trouts. This is one of the reasons it has been so widely transplanted throughout the world. It occurs naturally in Europe, from

Iceland and Norway to the Mediterranean, and also in Corsica, Sardinia, and Algeria, and as far east as the Himalayas. It has now been transplanted to most of the northern United States and to Canada, Argentina, South Africa, Ceylon, Australia, Tasmania, and New Zealand. It is not generally considered as fine a gamefish as other trouts, but its hardiness and ability to thrive under conditions unfavourable to other species make it a valuable fish.

There are sea-running races of brown trout, as well as those that remain in fresh water at all times. Those that spend part of their lives in salt water are quite differently coloured from the others, and once were thought to be a different species. Both kinds spawn only in fresh water, as do all other trout and salmon.

The eggs of the brown trout are spherical and a little less than one-fifth of an inch in diameter. Like the eggs of all trout and salmon, they are a little heavier than water and are slightly adhesive when first laid. They would be quickly washed downstream by the rapidly flowing current, were it not for the special manner in which they are laid. The female first digs a hole in the gravelly bottom that is six to eight inches deep to receive her eggs. This is the beginning of the trout nest, which is called a redd. When about to lay her eggs, the female sinks down to the bottom of the depression she has dug. The redd is so placed in relation to the current that the water passing over it produces a slight eddy. Therefore the water directly over the bottom where the eggs are laid actually moves upstream. This unexpected state of affairs was discovered by an investigator who placed crystals of potassium permanganate (a strongly coloured chemical) in redds that were being dug by brown trout, and discovered that the red-stained water travelled upstream, against the main current. This is the principal reason why the eggs are not washed away while they are being laid. The eggs stick to the bottom and this also helps prevent their being swept downstream. As soon as she has laid a batch of eggs, the female immediately starts to dig a new depression slightly upstream from the old one and in so doing displaces small stones and gravel that drop into the hole and soon cover the eggs completely. Safely resting under six to eight inches of clean gravel, the eggs are well protected from egg-eating fish and other animals and from smothering by mud or silt. Here they remain from forty to seventy days, when they hatch.

Brown trout spawn in the late autumn. They may reproduce seven

times during their lifetime and undoubtedly can survive more than
seven spawnings. Those that must endure the hardships of an upstream migration from the sea spawn less often than those living
entirely in fresh water. This species often attains weights of about
seven pounds, but has been known to reach thirty-nine and one-half
pounds.

The Brook Trout, *Salvelinus fontinalis,* is one of America's favourite
freshwater gamefish. Its delicious flesh, trim appearance, and brilliant
yet not gaudy colours, combined with its wariness and its spirit when
hooked, make it a fisherman's dream fish. Unfortunately this prince of
sportsfish requires pure, cold water and so has become increasingly
scarce as such waters have become more and more rare.

Brook trout vary greatly in size, depending on the supply of suitable
food and perhaps the size of the body of water in which they live. In
small streams or cold-water ponds the maximum weight ever attained
may be as little as one or even one-half pound. In rivers or lakes,
however, five-pound specimens may be regularly taken. The largest
brook trout ever caught weighed fourteen and one-half pounds.

Like most trout and salmon, brook trout eat a variety of foods. In
some places insects make up more than 90 per cent of their food. When
this is the case, brook trout rarely exceed nine inches in length. Larger
individuals feed mostly on other fishes and on crayfish, with an
occasional frog or salamander, although they continue to eat insects
when available.

Most brook trout remain in fresh water all their lives, but on the
north-eastern coast of the United States and Canada some of them
migrate to the sea for short periods. Spawning may take place in
flowing streams, quiet spring beds or gravelly shallows in lakes. Most
other species of trout and salmon depend on the fast flowing current
in which they construct their nests, or redds, to help them move
excavated material from the depression in which the eggs are laid, or
to help cover up the eggs after spawning. Since brook trout can spawn
in still waters, their behaviour is modified accordingly. Although
digging is apparently done in approximately the same manner by both
the brook trout and the Atlantic salmon, the female brook trout covers
her eggs with slow sweeps of her body, actually brushing small stones
and gravel over the eggs with her anal fin and tail.

Spawning takes place in October, November, and December, and the eggs usually hatch in February. One experimenter subjected captive brook trout to gradually decreasing amounts of light over a period of about a month. He found that they became ripe several months ahead of the regular spawning season. This indicates that the shortening of hours of daylight in the autumn is one of the principal stimulants to reproduction of the brook trout in nature. Brook trout have been crossed with brown trout in hatcheries; the hybrids are hardy, handsome fish, but apparently completely sterile.

Brook trout are native to eastern North America from Labrador to Georgia, and do not occur naturally west of the Mississippi except in parts of Iowa and Minnesota. They have now been introduced throughout the western United States and the provinces of Canada, and into parts of Europe, Argentina, and New Zealand. They belong to the group of trout known as chars, which in general are smaller than other trout, have a somewhat different arrangement of teeth from them, and possess smaller scales. As with all other trout and also the salmons, the natural home of the chars is in the fresh and salt waters of the northern part of the Northern Hemisphere.

The Lake Trout, *Salvelinus namaycush,* is the largest of all the trouts, and only one of the species of salmon equals or exceeds it in size. Individuals weighing twenty pounds are fairly common. The biggest specimen ever taken with rod and line weighed sixty-three pounds and was forty-seven and one-half inches long, but lake trout weighing about one hundred pounds have been caught commercially either with nets or set-lines.

Man has extended the range of this game and commercial fish by transplantation, so that it is now found both west and south of its former natural boundaries. In addition to lakes in the northern United States, Canada, and Alaska, lakes in California, the Pacific North-west, Peru, Bolivia, and New Zealand today harbour lake trout that were originally put there by man.

Lake trout often inhabit depths of eight hundred feet or more in larger lakes, but spawn during the autumn on gravel-covered or rocky areas in relatively shallow water. No nest or redd is constructed, although a common spawning area is cleaned by a number of fish, mostly males. No pairing takes place, and as many as three females and seven males may press together, spawning as a group. In captivity they have lived as long as twenty-four years.

The Red or Sockeye Salmon, *Oncorhynchus nerka,* forms an important part of the most valuable fishery resource of the United States. It is one of five species of Pacific salmon that yield around six hundred million pounds of fish each year to commercial fishermen in Oregon, Washington, and Alaska. It ranks second to the Pink Salmon, *Oncorhynchus gorbuscha,* in total quantity caught, but first in quality for canning.

Each year millions of salmon leave the sea and enter the streams in which they were hatched, travel as far as two thousand miles to spawning beds, lay their eggs, and then die. On their way upstream great numbers are caught in traps and nets, principally for canning. In recent years a grave new hazard to the successful completion of the Pacific salmon's life cycle has appeared, namely, great dams erected for hydro-electric power, irrigation, and flood control. Fish-ladders, elevators, and locks have been provided to permit fish to get over or bypass these otherwise insurmountable barriers. Nevertheless, enormous numbers of very young salmon, travelling down to the sea, are destroyed in the turbines and violent whirlpools of the dams themselves and in the irrigation ditches into which they are often diverted. For these and other reasons there has been a serious decline of salmon in many American rivers.

Regardless of whether they travel long or short distances or remain in fresh water all their lives, as a few of them do, the Pacific salmon all die very soon after spawning is completed. All pink salmon spawn when two years old, but the life span of the other species is more variable. Sockeye salmon range from three to eight years in age when they return to fresh water, the great majority of them being four or five. At this time they generally weigh about six pounds.

At sexual maturity the male sockeye salmon changes from a greenish or silvery blue to a blood-red body with a green head, while the female becomes a somewhat darker red. The male also develops a strongly hooked jaw, showing prominent teeth. Migration upstream takes place during the summer. Spawning occurs during the autumn, most often on gravelly shallows of tributaries to lakes. The female digs a nest, or redd, by lying on her side and rapidly vibrating her tail, thus creating currents that displace stones, gravel, and sand on the bottom. Both the female and male—the latter stands by, at least during the latter part of the nest building—defend the nesting site against other fishes. The male also frequently courts the female by gently nudging her with his snout, caressing her with his body and fins, and quivering by her side. During a female's spawning activities, several different males may be attendant on her, for the defending male is not always successful in driving off rival suitors and is sometimes himself driven off. When the saucer-like depression is completed, some eggs are laid and fertilized and immediately covered by the female. Several excavations, either immediately upstream from the first one or in some new locality, may be made before all the eggs of a single female are laid.

Young sockeye salmon appear in the spring. They pass down to the lakes and usually remain there for a year, sometimes two or three, before they proceed to the sea. At all sizes sockeye salmon feed principally on small aquatic crustaceans.

In many lakes in the Far West there are sockeye salmon that never enter salt water. These are usually much smaller than ocean-going ones. Some of them have been introduced into one or two places in Maine, Pennsylvania, Connecticut, and New Zealand.

The Lake Whitefish, *Coregonus clupeaformis*, is still one of the most valuable of freshwater foodfishes in North America, even though the catch has become greatly reduced in numbers—presumably from overfishing. It is generally distributed through the Great Lakes and various smaller lakes in Maine, New York, Michigan, Wisconsin, Minnesota, and all the Canadian provinces as far north as Alaska. In the region of Hudson's Bay it spends considerable time in brackish water. To the natives of Northern Canada the whitefish is an important source of food and is preferred above all other fishes.

Lake whitefish are more or less oval or spindle shaped, with an olive back and silvery sides and belly. Considerable variability in size, shape and other characteristics is found from area to area and sometimes even from lake to lake. A maximum size of twenty-six pounds has been recorded. In some places maturity is not reached until the fish weigh three pounds; in others mature fish weighing less than an ounce are known.

Spawning usually takes place in the autumn in relatively shallow water. The eggs are heavier than water and lie on the bottom. Hatching takes place after approximately twenty weeks. The food of the lake whitefish consists of crustaceans, aquatic insects, molluscs, and, to a lesser extent, small fishes.

There are about thirty-five different species of whitefishes and their close relatives, the ciscos and tullibees. They are found around the polar regions, in the salt waters of the extreme north, and in the fresh waters of northern Europe, Asia, and North America.

The American Smelt, *Osmerus mordax*, usually spends most of its life in the sea, coming into fresh water only to spawn. There are, however, a number of places in which it is landlocked, that is, in which it has no access to the ocean and therefore spends its whole life in fresh water.

It occurs naturally on the Atlantic coast from Labrador to New York and in the St. Lawrence River, Lake Champlain, Lake Ontario, and their associated streams. About 1912 it was introduced into the other Great Lakes, where it gradually became more and more abundant. At first it was thought that the smelt would eventually outstrip most of the native fishes and become a pest, and its exact effect on fishes like lake trout is still debated. After the smelt had increased sufficiently, however, a valuable fishery developed, and many millions of pounds were taken both by commercial and sports fishermen. Then in the early 1940's almost all the smelt in the upper Great Lakes disappeared. The reason for this remains a mystery, although there is a little evidence that some epidemic disease was responsible. Today, apparently, the smelt is slowly coming back.

American smelt are caught in a variety of ways: by hook and line, by dipping with hand-nets while they proceed upstream to spawn, by gill nets, and with special nets set under the ice. Smelt may attain a size of somewhat more than a foot, but most adults are considerably smaller.

Spawning takes place in very early spring, sometimes just after ice has left the water. Smelt that have been living in salt water do not go far upstream, even spawning in slightly salty water in certain instances. Those that live permanently in fresh water spawn in small streams or the shallow parts of lakes. During egg laying a single female is generally attended by several males. The eggs are sticky when first laid and adhere to any aquatic plants, sticks, stones, or gravel that they touch.

In all, there are roughly a dozen species of smelt and their relatives, the capelina and eulachon, inhabiting the northern seas around Asia, Scandinavia, Canada, and Alaska.

The Atlantic Capelin, *Mallotus villosus,* runs on to beaches out of water to spawn. During the late spring, schools of capelin gather just beyond the waves breaking on gravelly beaches. There, the males seek out the females, each one attaching himself to the side of his prospective mate, or two males flanking a single female on either side. Together they swim vigorously toward the shore just ahead of an incoming wave. As they settle on the beach, they scoop out a small hollow with rapid strokes of their tails, and then the eggs are laid and fertilized. The spawning act takes only a few seconds and may be completed in time for the fish, by paddling furiously toward the deeper water, to ride the same wave back out to sea, or they may have to wait for the succeeding one.

Male capelin are slightly larger than females and have longer pectoral fins. During the reproductive season they exhibit along their sides two rows of pointed scales covered with thickened skin. It is by means of these ridges that the males are able to cling to the females during spawning.

The average female capelin lays about thirty thousand eggs. These eggs, each about one thirty-second of an inch in diameter, are adhesive and become attached to bits of sand or gravel. Most of them are probably buried in the gravel of the beach by the action of the waves, but a good many are washed to sea or eventually exposed to sun and air.

In the water, they are eaten by winter flounders and other fishes, including capelin themselves, and on dry land they are destroyed by maggots, drying out, and high temperatures. Those eggs that are properly protected hatch in two weeks to a month, depending on the temperature. Capelin also spawn in water somewhat off-shore, generally laying their eggs over sandy bottoms.

Spawning capelin average about seven inches long. Their maximum length is about nine inches, and they ordinarily live to be from five to seven years old. They feed on small creatures floating in the sea. Capelin habitually live out in the ocean, coming inshore only during the spawning season. In their migrations they are followed by large numbers of Atlantic cod, which sometimes pursue them almost on to the beaches. Not only do cod feed voraciously upon them, but Atlantic salmon and other fishes, as well as seals and sea-birds, live largely upon capelin at certain times of the year.

In Newfoundland, the capelin is taken in great numbers during the spawning season. Salted and dried, smoked, fresh, or frozen, it is used for human consumption. It is also used fresh for cod bait, and large amounts are employed as fertilizer. The fish is also of economic importance in Finland and other countries where spawning runs take place.

The capelin inhabits the north Atlantic and Arctic Oceans from Hudson Bay to Scandinavia. It occurs as far south as the coast of Maine, but rarely spawns there. The closely related Pacific Capelin, *Mallotus catervarius*, is found in the north Pacific and Arctic Oceans as far south in the east as the state of Washington.

The Pike, *Esox lucius*, often lies in wait for its prey, and when some unsuspecting fish swims by its weedy lair, it dashes out with split-second speed to snap it up. Sometimes, instead of lying in wait, it stalks its prey, the stealthy approach being followed by the same death-dealing sprint. The pike's great voracity is well known; fishes large and small, frogs, snakes, crayfish, and even birds and mammals have been found in its stomach. Small specimens feed on crustaceans, worms, and insect larvae. They become principally fish-eaters when they grow up. Pikes consume an enormous amount of food in the course of a year.

The long, sturdy body of the pike is usually olive or greenish grey with light yellow spots on the sides, shading into the whitish or yellowish belly. Younger specimens are marked with light bars rather than spots. A greenish, silvery variety of pike showing no pattern at all has recently appeared in Minnesota waters. The pointed jaws of the pike are lined with numerous sharp teeth. Although teeth that are broken off or worn down are replaced, the idea that the fish sheds its teeth regularly each summer has definitely been proved untrue. As in many species of fishes that catch their prey by making short dashes, the dorsal and anal fins are located towards the rear, near the tail.

Pikes are found throughout the Northern Hemisphere in Europe (excepting Spain and Portugal), northern Asia, and in North America south to British Columbia, Montana, Nebraska, Missouri, the Ohio valley, and New York. They prefer quiet, weedy waters. The record pike caught by rod-and-reel weighed forty-six pounds, two ounces, and was fifty-two and one-half inches long. Specimens weighing more than fifty pounds are known. Pikes are most frequently taken by trolling, that is, fishing with a hook that is drawn along or through the water, but they may also be still-fished with live bait. In winter they are lured, then speared through the ice. Besides being a highly esteemed gamefish, the pike is a foodfish of minor importance.

Soon after the ice melts in early spring the pike spawns. Numerous barely adhesive eggs, heavier than water and not quite three-sixteenths of an inch in diameter are laid, usually among plants or decaying vegetation. Spawning generally occurs in shallow water during day-light hours, each female being accompanied by one, two or three males. Hatching occurs in one to four weeks, depending on the temperature. Hybrids between the pike and the muskellunge and the chain pickerel are found in nature, undoubtedly resulting from the fact that they may sometimes carry on their reproductive activities in the same area at the same time.

The Muskellunge, *Esox masquinongy*, is one of the prize gamefish of North America. It attains a weight of over one hundred pounds, and specimens weighing more than fifty pounds are caught every year. The official record fish caught by means of angler's tackle weighed sixty-four and one-half pounds and was fifty-eight inches long. Like the pike, the muskellunge is a savage fighter.

The muskellunge is often confused with the pike, but can usually be distinguished by its lack of scales below the level of the eye on both the lower cheeks and gill-covers. The pike lacks them only on the gill-covers, its cheeks being fully scaled. The scales on the body of the muskellunge are also relatively smaller than those on the pike; the sensory pores under the lower jaw are smaller and more numerous; and the number of rays under the gill-covers is greater. There are also differences in colour pattern and in shape of head and body, but these are less pronounced and liable to be misleading. In general, however, muskellunge tend to be darker than pike and to carry dark spots or bars rather than light ones.

Fully as voracious as the pike, the muskellunge leads the same sort of life. It generally prefers somewhat colder and deeper waters, how-ever, and tends to be more solitary in habit. It spawns a little later than does the pike, and in open waters, rather than among weeds. Both species' spawning areas and seasons overlap sometimes, which explains the presence of natural hybrids between the two. Muskellunge can grow very fast; when only two months old they may be six inches long. Such specimens eat ten to fifteen minnows every day.

The Central Mudminnow, *Umbra limi*, manages well even under the worst of living conditions. It can exist in stagnant pools, and, if these dry up, it burrows into the mud and awaits the return of water. Neither high nor low temperatures greatly inconvenience it; it is often the only species of fish to survive a very severe freeze. In fact, it is frequently the only fish ever to be found in the shallow, muddy ponds, swamps, and bog-pools it inhabits. Mudminnows are also found in more favourable surroundings, most often among plants and over muddy bottoms.

Mudminnows eat a great variety of small objects, both animal and vegetable, living and dead, although they are principally flesh eaters. They are small fish, seldom exceeding four inches in length. At first glance they appear to be a drab dark brown, but close examination reveals a rather attractive mottled pattern.

It is the female mudminnow who takes care of the nest and eggs, guarding them and carefully picking out and devouring any that do not develop. In all other North American fishes that build nests, it is the male who keeps house, although in a few of the catfishes both parents may share that task. Spawning takes place in the spring.

The central mudminnow ranges through the Great Lakes region, east to Lake Champlain and south to Tennessee and has been transplanted to parts of north-western Europe. Another closely related species of mudminnow is found along the Atlantic Coast.

Minnows, Characins, Catfishes and Their Relatives

THE BULK of our freshwater fishes—the creatures that throng the lakes and streams of the world—are members of this great group. The minnows, characins, catfishes, and all their motley array of relatives comprise it—they total perhaps five thousand different species, all

[12-7]

Some 5,000 species of highly diversified, freshwater fish are classified in one order because whatever else they lack in common, they have a chain of small bones connecting the inner ear to the air bladder. The order is divided into three main groups and to one of these belong the suckers. Two of the 90-odd species are found in Asia, but the remainder are North American fish. Bottom-feeders, suckers consume the eggs of other fish when and where they are available, but in turn they serve as food for various important commercial fish and gamefish.   See page 1455

[12-7A]

The redhorse sucker of the clear northern streams and lakes is generally considered to be the tastiest species from the human standpoint. They grow to a length of two feet and may weigh as much as eight or ten pounds. The "shark suckers" belong to an entirely different family.   See page 1457

[12-8]

Minnows and carp are grouped with the suckers. The common shiner is one of the most abundant of North American minnows, inhabiting streams and lakes throughout the continent east of the Rockies, from southern Canada and Maine to the Gulf States and North Carolina. It reaches a length of eight inches, and is widely used as a bait fish.   *See page 1459*

[12-8A]

During the spawning season (spring and early summer), the sides of the male common shiner become tinged with red and his other colouring becomes more intensified. Males gather on gravel and sand beds in streams to await the appearance of the females, and whether they construct nests or not, they constantly fight each other for the best position in the area. Frequently common shiners lay their eggs in the nests of other minnows, giving rise to several kinds of well-known natural hybrids.

See page 1459

[12-9]

The golden shiner gets its name from the breeding colour of the male. Somewhat smaller than the common shiner (they average about five inches in length), they are hardier than most of the family and are much better able to survive in small ponds during the winter. Shiners feed on the bottom, at the surface, and in mid-water, consuming both plant and animal matter.   *See page 1459*

[12-9A]

Chub are included in the more than 400 species that make up the North American minnow family. Averaging about a foot in length, they are sometimes taken as sports fish when trout are scarce. Chub only occasionally invade the lakes, preferring the moving water of creeks and rivers.   *See page 1458*

[12-10]

The natural home of the wild goldfish is in southern China, and the Chinese first domesticated these carplike fish a thousand years ago. The amazing results that can sometimes be obtained through selective breeding are well demonstrated with goldfish, an astonishing number of differently coloured and shaped types having been developed. These fish quickly revert to the wild state, all the beautiful, fancy-coloured individuals disappearing; they may grow to a length of two feet and their feeding habits make them a nuisance and even a threat to native fish. *See page 1464*

[12-10A]

While some groups of fish have an accessory direct air-breathing apparatus, the majority obtain oxygen by means of gill systems. Water is taken in through the mouth and passed through the gills, which extract the oxygen and throw off carbon dioxide; the water then moves out through the openings under the gill covers. With very few exceptions, fish use their nostrils to smell and not to breathe. The fish pictured here is a carp. Originally a native of Asia, the carp is now found on all the continents, and while it tends to compete severely with native forms, the harm it does is offset by the fact that it provides people with wholesome, high-protein food at a reasonable cost. *See page 1462*

told. Among them we find dwarfs as well as giants, and maximum size ranges from a scant one inch to as much as ten feet.

One might well be puzzled by the meaning of the scientific name of the group: "little bones-bladder" (order Ostariophysi). But it does describe the outstanding feature of all of the fishes in this order: the Weberian apparatus, a chain of small bones which connect the fish's inner ear with its air bladder. We suppose these help it to detect movements, sounds, and changes in pressure.

Three main groups of fishes are included in this group: the first made up of the suckers and buffalo fishes (family Catostomidae), the minnows, carps, barbs, etc. (Cyprinidae), and the loaches and weather fish (Cobitidae); in the second we place the tetras, piranhas, hatchet fishes, etc. (Characidae), and their relatives, including the electric eel and other gymnotid eels (Gymnotidae); and the third is composed of the dozen or more families of catfishes.

The suckers are mostly from North America, with only two species found in Asia. The cyprinids hail from Asia, Europe, North America, and Africa. Loaches inhabit Asia, Europe, and northern Africa. The characins range from Texas through Central America and most of South America, and are well known in Africa; while the gymnotid eels are found only in South and Central America. Unlike the other groups, the catfishes are found in both salt and fresh waters. About two thousand species of them occur in warm salt and brackish waters all over the world, and in the streams and lakes of every continent.

The characins are a most varied group—we find them ranging in size from one-inch midgets to six-foot monsters, and from inoffensive vegetarians to voracious flesh-eaters, such as the piranhas and the Goliath Tiger Fish, *Hydrocyon goliath*, of tropical Africa, which is the largest of all the characins. Some characins are shaped like minnows, some like darters, pikes, or snakeheads, and many have contours different from any other fish. A number of the smaller, brightly coloured species are popular with tropical fish fanciers. Most species lay small, more or less adhesive eggs, and show no parental care of either eggs or young. A few, however, build nests and guard their eggs. One great oddity, the Splashing Samlet, *Copeina arnoldi*, lays its eggs out of water on overhanging leaves. The dutiful male remains near the eggs and periodically splashes water upon them to keep them moist.

There are about fifty species of gymnotid eels, the largest of which is the famous electric eel, the only one with great electrical powers.

EAL / 12—E

The other species seldom exceed three feet in length, but all the species have long bodies, with the vital organs confined to the front one-fifth of the body. Dorsal and tail fins are lacking; the principal means of locomotion is the long anal fin, which is undulated, enabling the fish to move either forward or backward—seemingly with equal ease.

The catfishes range in size from tiny, one-inch species to those reaching lengths of ten feet and weights of well over six hundred pounds. Their great variety of body forms and the many structural peculiarities shown by them defy brief description, and their habits, if anything, are even more varied. A few are equipped with unique devices for breathing atmospheric air, enabling them to live in mud-holes and swamps, and even out of water, for long periods. Some of these, and other catfishes, too, can "sleep" through a dry season in the mud at the bottom of a dried-up stream or pond, and live for months without food or water in a state of suspended animation. A few can travel on land, and do so for fair distances. In one African family, there are species that habitually swim upside down.

There are more than a dozen blind catfishes—a greater number than in any other group of fishes. Most of them inhabit caves, but two or three burrow in the bottom of open streams. There are tiny catfishes no bigger than one-inch toothpicks that live in the gills of other fishes, sucking blood from them. Others gnaw holes through the sides of larger fishes in order to obtain blood—somewhat like the way in which the lampreys feed.

Reproductive habits among the catfishes are also most variable. Many construct nests and care for their eggs—and sometimes for their young, too. One or two species build a raftlike affair of plants and frothlike bubbles which are blown by the fish, to hold the eggs. In one whole group the males carry the eggs and young in their mouths for as long as two months—until they are well developed and able to fend for themselves. A few female catfishes carry their eggs in a layer attached to their bellies, and some armoured catfish males carry the eggs in enlarged folds of their lips. Still other catfishes simply lay their eggs on plants or stones, and pay no more attention to them.

The White Sucker, *Catostomus commersoni*, has often been accused of consuming large quantities of the eggs of trout, but there is no proof for this—no eggs have been found in the stomachs of white suckers, nor have these fish been observed eating trout eggs. It is true, however, that white suckers eat the eggs of other fishes when they are available; apparently trout eggs are not easily obtained by them. Other foods of this species include insect larvae, molluscs, crustaceans, worms, and algae and other aquatic plants.

The mouth of the white sucker is located underneath its short, blunt snout, and, as you might expect, a great deal of its food is procured from the bottom. The body is slender and cylindrical. In males it becomes darker during the spawning season and develops a black band lying along the side above a rose-coloured one. In the early spring, white suckers leave the lakes, pools, and rivers where they usually live, and crowd into smaller streams to spawn in swift water over gravelly bottoms. Occasionally they also lay their eggs in quiet pools. The eggs are pale yellowish in colour and about three thirty-seconds of an inch in diameter when first laid. Being heavier than water, they come to rest among the pieces of gravel, where they remain from five to twenty days, depending on the temperature, before they hatch. During spawning, two or more males flank the larger female, pressing against her sides. They are helped to maintain their position by the many tiny, hard, conical growths, called "pearl organs", that develop along their bodies and fins during the time for breeding.

White suckers are widely distributed east of the Rocky Mountains from Labrador and the Mackenzie River system in northern Canada, south to the Gulf states. Their greatest importance is as a forage fish, that is, as food for various commercial and gamefishes. They are eaten by man, however, in fair quantities in some places, being taken mostly during the spawning migration. They reach a length of over twenty inches. Because they multiply rapidly—more than one hundred thousand eggs may be produced by a large female—and are easily raised in fish hatcheries, white suckers are becoming increasingly important as bait fish.

The suckers, including the buffalo fishes, chubsuckers, redhorse suckers, and quillback, make up a family of nearly ninety species.

The Bigmouth Buffalo Fish, *Megastomatobus cyprinella*, prefers the sluggish waters of large rivers, bayous, and shallow lakes. It ranges from southern Canada to Texas and is most common in the Mississippi valley. It has been transplanted into southern California.

The bigmouth buffalo fish is a stocky fish with an elliptical body. The mouth is sharply angled upwards. Its food consists of both vegetable and animal matter, the latter including insect larvae and molluscs. Reproduction takes place in the spring, when the bigmouth buffalo fish lays adhesive eggs which hatch in about nine days at 60° Fahrenheit.

Buffalo fishes are the basis of one of the most valuable of North American inland fisheries. There are three or four species of commercial importance, of which the bigmouth buffalo fish is probably the most numerous and definitely the largest. In fact it is the largest species of all the suckers, reaching a length of four feet and a weight of sixty-five pounds.

The North American Minnows are the most numerous single group of freshwater fishes on that continent—and one of the most important, too. Most of them do not reach a large size, but they provide the bulk of the food for practically all the larger fish-eating commercial and gamefishes. A few, such as the Fallfish, exceed one foot, and the relatively gigantic Colorado Squawfish, *Ptychocheilus lucius*, attains a length of five feet and a weight of eighty pounds.

The squawfishes are fish-eaters, but most minnows feed on very small animals and on aquatic plants. Minnows inhabit many different types of water, from glacial lakes to warm springs and from tiny mountain brooks to broad silted rivers. Included in the more than four hundred different species are the shiners, chubs, dace, stonerollers, squawfishes, and the hitch.

Minnows are often mistaken for the young of larger fishes, but can be distinguished from them by their lack of teeth on the jaws (they have instead a few large teeth in their throats), the presence of a Weberian apparatus (as described earlier), the absence of scales on the head, the location of the pelvic fins back towards the rear of the body, the lack of spines in any of the fins, and the presence of less than ten main fin rays in the single dorsal fin. Any fish not having all these characteristics is not a North American minnow.

The reproductive habits of these minnows are quite variable. In a number of species, the males excavate shallow pits in gravel or sand to receive the eggs. In others they gather piles of small stones to make a nest. Among these species is the Fallfish, *Semotilus corporalis*. Although the males never exceed eighteen inches, they perform great feats of strength in moving large stones—as much as three and one-half inches in diameter—and may construct a nest eighteen feet in circumference and three feet high at the centre. Still other species of minnows lay their eggs in crevices of logs or on the under-surfaces of stones and other submerged objects, after which they are guarded and cared for by the male. Finally, there is a whole group that builds no nest of any sort and shows no parental care, simply allowing the eggs to fall on gravel or sand or into aquatic vegetation. Among those species that build nests, the males are usually larger than the females and develop beautiful, bright coloration during the spawning season, which is in spring or summer. At this time they also develop small horny growths, the pearl organs.

The North American minnows belong to the family Cyprinidae, of which the rasboras, danios, bitterlings, carps, goldfish, barbs, gudgeon, and roach are also members. This is the largest single family of fishes, containing roughly two thousand species. A species, *Catlocarpio siamensis*, from south-eastern Asia, reaches lengths of nearly ten feet, and is the largest of all the cyprinids.

The Common Shiner, *Notropis cornutus*, is one of the most abundant of North American minnows and is widely used as a bait fish. It is found in many streams and lakes throughout the continent east of the Rockies, from southern Canada and Maine to the Gulf states and North Carolina. It reaches a length of eight inches.

Males are generally larger than females, and during the spawning season their sides become tinged with red, and their other colours become intensified. Females remain practically the same colour all the year round, that is, olive green or grey above and silvery below. Males also develop breeding tubercles around the head, on the back, and on the pectoral fins; these are undoubtedly of use in fighting, digging and mating.

During spring and early summer males gather on gravel or sand beds in streams, awaiting the appearance of females ready to spawn. Sometimes nests up to about one foot in diameter are dug, by inserting the head between small stones and dislodging them, thus cleaning away the silt and sometimes creating a slight depression. Whether or not a nest is constructed, the males constantly vie with one another for the best position in the area. They rush around one another, trying to butt their rivals, and also indulge in a kind of display behaviour in which two opponents tensely swim together side by side for a few feet before returning to the spawning area. Usually the largest male

holds the position farthest upstream, with perhaps twenty others
jockeying for position behind him. When a female appears near a male
on the spawning ground, he displays to her in a peculiar manner, and
they embrace for a fraction of a second during which time perhaps
fifty orange-coloured eggs about one-sixteenth of an inch in diameter
are laid. These soon become adhesive and stick to pebbles and grains
of sand.

Frequently common shiners use the nests of other species of minnows
as places in which to lay their eggs. It is undoubtedly this habit that
leads to the production of the several kinds of well-known hybrids,
involving the common shiner and other minnows. Scientists believe
that when common shiners happen to spawn at the same moment a
pair of some other species is doing so, the sexual elements may become
mixed in the water, creating natural hybrids.

Common shiners feed at the surface, on the bottom, and in mid-
water. They consume both plant and animal matter. The former consists mostly of algae and tiny plants called "diatoms"; the latter includes
many insects and crustaceans, worms, and small fishes.

The Bluntnose Minnow, *Hyborhynchus notatus*, lays its eggs on the
under-surface of such natural objects as rocks, logs, strips of bark, and
mussel shells, and artificial ones like boards, tile, tin cans, and pieces
of flat metal or tar-paper. The male prepares the nesting site by
hollowing out a cavity beneath the object just big enough for him to
enter and then cleaning off the lower surface where the eggs will be
attached. Several females lay in a single nest, usually at night, and as
many as five thousand eggs may finally be present in a large one. The
male guards the eggs most bravely, protecting them from other fishes
and from leeches and snails. He also circulates water around them
and keeps them free from sediment. Frequently several males build
their nests alongside one another, each fish apparently recognizing
his own place and living at peace with his neighbours.

The male bluntnose minnow assumes a darker coloration at the
onset of the time for breeding. He also develops three rows of hard,
conical growths across the rounded snout. These protuberances are
used in nest-digging and in butting other fishes. The spawning season
extends through the spring and summer. The eggs are about one-
sixteenth of an inch in diameter and are adhesive. They hatch in from
six days to two weeks, and the young are about one-fifth of an inch long.

No parental care over them is shown. Male bluntnose minnows grow to be about four inches long, females about three. Some live to be at least four years old. They feed mostly on tiny plants and animals.

The range of the bluntnose minnow includes most of the eastern half of the United States and Canada, from Quebec and North Dakota to Virginia and the Gulf States. Because of their large numbers, wide distribution, and ability to withstand different living conditions, bluntnose minnows are among the most important forage minnows. Since they do not compete with gamefishes for food to any extent, yet provide them with excellent food themselves, they may be considered doubly valuable.

The Red Rasbora, *Rasbora heteromorpha*, occurs in streams and lakes of Sumatra, the Malay Peninsula, and Thailand. It is perhaps the best-known member of the very numerous group of small, fresh-water fishes called rasboras. Its renown arises from its beauty and its ability to thrive in home aquaria. Since 1906, the year it was first imported alive into Europe, it has been one of the most popular of the fishes kept as pets.

Red rasboras reach a length of about one and three-quarter inches. Their bodies are tinged with a lovely rose colour, over which a delicate, shifting rainbow plays. Each side, from the mid-point of the body to the tail, carries a roughly triangular, purplish-black mark, which contrasts beautifully with the rest of the fish. Above this is a golden line, usually more brilliant in males than females. The fins are tinted red and yellow.

The adhesive eggs are usually laid on the under-side of the leaves of aquatic plants. The mating pair turn on their backs to deposit and fertilize them. The eggs hatch in about one and one-half days.

The Bitterling, *Rhodeus amarus*, uses a living freshwater mussel as a nursery. At spawning time in the spring, the female grows a long tube or ovipositor that may become as long as she is, that is, about three inches. Both the male, who assumes a bright red nuptial livery, and the female indulge in courtship behaviour in which they seem to pay much more attention to some particular mussel lying half exposed on the bottom than to each other. Suddenly, with a motion so fast that its exact details are still a matter of question, the female inserts her ovipositor into the exhalant or excurrent siphon (the tube that discharges water) of the bivalved mollusc and lays one or two ellipsoidal eggs inside. The male immediately performs his part, the eggs being fertilized while inside the mollusc. This procedure is repeated many times over the course of several days, more than one mussel being used by a single female. The eggs become lodged among the gills of the mussel, and two to three weeks later, tiny bitterlings emerge from their strange shelter.

LAYING EGGS IN A MUSSEL

The bitterling uses a living freshwater mussel as a nursery. After the female has laid her eggs in the mussel, the male fertilizes them there. This fish, a native of central Europe, was introduced into New York waters and thrived there for some time, using American mussels for its eggs.

Bitterlings are found in central Europe. They use at least two different species of European mussels as a hatching place for their eggs. For a while at least, they successfully maintained themselves in the United States after being introduced into New York waters. It was found that two different American mussels could also be utilized by the fish. There are several Asiatic species of bitterling-like fishes, including three or four from Japan.

The Carp, *Cyprinus carpio,* has proved a mixed blessing to man, but the good service it has done far outweighs the bad. It has provided countless people with wholesome, high-protein food at most reasonable cost. Although considered inferior in taste and too full of bones by many—including most North Americans—the fact remains that the fish is delicious when properly prepared.

Even in the United States, where carp are considered an inferior foodfish by the great majority of people, more than seventeen million pounds are caught annually, mostly for food. The carp is by far the most important species employed in the extensive culturing of fishes in ponds that is carried on in Europe and the Near East, and is one of the most important in the Far East. It is also raised for food in parts of South America and Africa. No accurate estimate of present-day, world-wide consumption of carp has ever been made; nevertheless, it is safe to say that more carp are eaten by man than any other fresh-water fish.

Originally a native of Asia—and probably of Europe, too—the carp is now found on all the continents, and also in outlying places like Madagascar and the Hawaiian Islands. Some authorities believe it was introduced into Europe during the thirteenth century. In 1872 a few specimens were carried from Germany to California; four or five years later some were brought over to Maryland. With much enthusiasm and little discretion carp were soon transplanted into the waters of most states. The species was introduced into Africa and South America somewhat later. In many of these places carp have become a nuisance or actually a menace to other, more valuable, kinds of fishes. Because of their hardiness, adaptability, and high breeding rate, carp tend to compete severely with native forms and, sometimes, to replace them. They destroy vegetation and thus the breeding grounds and shelters of many species, but worst of all, their habit of rooting up the bottom for food can so stir up and cloud the water with sediment as to render it unsuitable for desirable fishes.

Carp were undoubtedly the first of all fish to be domesticated; the Chinese have raised them in ponds for at least twenty-five hundred years. There are three principal varieties used in pond culture today: the mirror carp, which has a reduced number of scales, scattered over the body with bare skin in between; the leather carp, which has no scales at all or only very few around the base of the fins; and the fully scaled, wild type. A number of special strains have also been developed, showing varying degrees of rapidity of growth, economical use of food, resistance to disease, and the like. Under good domestic conditions, carp attain a weight of three pounds by the time they are three years old. If carp ponds are fertilized to increase the growth of microscopic plants and animals and the fish are artificially fed, they will yield as much as twelve hundred pounds of fish per acre each year. Since carp are primarily vegetarian, they can use plants directly as food, although they will eat a variety of small animals and animal products as well.

The eggs of the carp are about one-sixteenth of an inch in diameter. They are adhesive, and in nature are laid on water plants. Spawning takes place in spring and early summer, often being accompanied by much splashing and other commotion as the female swims about, closely attended by several males. Females can produce tremendous quantities of eggs, all of which, however, may not be laid at one time. Hatching occurs from about five to twenty days after laying, the length of time depending on the temperature of the water.

Carp live well in captivity; some specimens have been kept alive for more than thirty years. A maximum weight of eighty-three and one-half pounds has been reported, but rarely is forty pounds exceeded.

The Goldfish, *Carassius auratus,* was first domesticated by the Chinese one thousand years ago. Wild goldfish are more or less dull silver and bronze in colour—similar to the carp, to which they are related, but from which they are entirely distinct, even though the two species can cross. Comparing the two, carp can be identified by the presence of two pairs of short barbels on the upper jaw. In nature, goldfish often show a golden condition, apparently resulting from the reduction or lack of black pigment cells; it was from such specimens that the first domestic yellow-gold or red-gold fish were developed. The natural home of the wild goldfish is in southern China, and both young and old are used for food there today.

Various fancy strains, such as fantails and veiltails, were originated by the Chinese relatively early, and the Japanese carried on this work after the introduction of goldfish into their country at about the beginning of the sixteenth century. It is not definitely known when the goldfish was first brought to Europe, but evidence indicates that it was imported into England during the first half of the eighteenth century.

By about 1785 goldfish bowls had become popular household decorations in this country. Goldfish may have been taken to the United

States as early as 1850; at any rate some had already escaped into the Schuylkill River by 1858. Unfortunately, when these fish revert to the wild state, all the beautiful, fancy-coloured individuals disappear, leaving only dull, unprepossessing fish with feeding habits that make them a nuisance and even a threat to native fishes. Wild goldfish are now also found in Europe, Madagascar, Hawaii, Australia, and much of the Orient.

The goldfish are omnivorous, that is, they eat all sorts of animal and vegetable matter; most people that keep them do not realize the great variety of foodstuffs their pets will consume if given the opportunity. Goldfish have no jaw teeth and so can eat only small items and soft materials like algae. Much time is spent grubbing and picking about the bottom, and this is what makes them undesirable tenants in natural waters. Goldfish should never be allowed to escape into the wilds because they can easily become a pest.

Spawning takes place in the spring and summer. Males develop numerous, small growths on the head, gill covers, and pectoral fins; and females become heavy with eggs. The eggs are adhesive and are scattered on plants as the female swims through them, pursued by one or more males. A medium-sized fish lays as many as one thousand eggs at a single spawning and may spawn more than once in a season. At about 60 degrees, hatching occurs in nine days. Newly hatched fry are about one-fifth of an inch long, and have a prominent yolk-sac. They do little or no swimming for the first two days, while the yolk is being absorbed, but then they start actively to search for microscopic and near-microscopic food. Goldfish have lived long lives in captivity—for at least twenty years on good authority. The ordinary ones can reach lengths of two feet, but rarely do so because they are confined in relatively small tanks or pools.

The amazing results that can sometimes be obtained through selective breeding cannot be better shown than with the goldfish. An astonishing number of differently coloured and shaped types have been developed at one time or another during the long history of this fish as a domestic animal. There are red-, orange-, yellow-, blue-, and black-hued strains. Fish lacking dorsal or tail fins have been bred. Enormously enlarged fins, some of them doubled, are well known. Fish with telescopic eyes, with shortened, egg-shaped or comma-shaped bodies, or with large wartlike growths on the head have been developed. Perfect examples of some of these types are extremely difficult to obtain, since thousands of individuals must be weeded out—even among the offspring of specially selected parents—before the right one is found. Such fish have sold for as much as seven hundred dollars each.

The Barbel, *Barbus barbus*, is the only member of the large group of barbs found north of the Alps. The great majority of the several hundred different species come from Africa and tropical Asia eastward to the East Indies. We find the barbel in France and Germany and other central and southern European countries as well as in a few rivers of eastern England.

The body of the barbel is rather long. Its mouth is crescent-shaped with thick lips and is located on the under-side of the snout. There are two pairs of barbels, one on the snout, the other at the corners of the mouth. The barbel usually feeds by grubbing on the bottom for a large variety of animal and vegetable matter.

In May and June barbels spawn, laying eggs, which are heavier than water, over gravelly bottoms. The eggs of the barbel are believed to be more or less poisonous, and it is considered good practice to remove them from a female fish very soon after catching.

The barbel is one of the medium-sized barbs. Many of this group are small—of a size that perfectly suits them for home aquaria. A few are very large, the mahseers of India, for example. These are famous gamefishes that attain weights well over one hundred pounds and perhaps exceed two hundred. In England the maximum recorded weight of the barbel is twenty pounds, but larger specimens are known on the Continent.

The Gudgeon, *Gobio gobio*, is a small, bottom-inhabiting fish of streams, lakes, and ponds in England, Wales, and Ireland, and on the Continent, excepting Greece, Spain, and Portugal. Towards the east, it is found in Russia, Turkestan, Siberia, and Mongolia. It rarely exceeds six inches in length, although specimens two inches longer are known.

The gudgeon has a small crescent-shaped mouth located on the under-side of the snout, with a single barbel on either side. Its food consists of small crustaceans and molluscs, insect larvae, worms, and fish eggs and fry. During the spring and summer gudgeons lay their small, adhesive eggs on gravelly shallows. Despite its dimunitive size, the gudgeon fights gamely when hooked. Comparatively speaking, though, fishermen have always considered it an easy fish to catch. As a result its name has become a synonym for a creature that may be duped without trouble—Shakespeare used the word that way. The gudgeon makes a delightful morsel when cooked, but many prefer to use it as a bait fish.

The Roach, *Rutilus rutilus,* is probably the most sought after of all freshwater fishes in England and Scotland; more anglers try their skill against this species than any other. In most places, catching roach requires both skill and patience, for the fish are quite wary. Unfortunately, once caught, they are not too well liked for food because of their bony flesh and sometimes muddy flavour. The record specimen ever caught by rod-and-reel weighed three pounds, fourteen ounces. Such a fish is about eighteen inches long. Individuals more than two pounds in weight are uncommon, and any roach over one pound is considered a good catch.

Roach inhabit quiet fresh waters in northern Europe and Asia. Sometimes they also are found in brackish waters. They feed on vegetable and animal matter, usually near the bottom. Spawning takes place in the spring, when the fish migrate from deeper waters, where they have spent the winter, to weedy shallows or small streams. They lay numerous small eggs, which are heavier than water and which hatch in about eleven days. The roach can hybridize with at least three different fishes of its own family in Europe and the British Isles, and these hybrids have been found in nature.

The Weather Fish, *Misgurnus fossilis,* is supposed to indicate coming changes in the weather by dashing frantically around its tank. The fish makes an interesting aquatic pet, but its ability as a weather prophet seems to have been exaggerated.

Weather fish inhabit fresh waters of central Europe, east to the region of the Caspian Sea. They are bottom forms that hide for most of the daylight hours, sometimes digging their long, thin, round bodies into mud or sand. A length of at least twenty inches is sometimes reached. The weather fish employs its intestine for breathing atmospheric air in addition to the more usual respiration by means of gills. It rises to the surface and swallows some air which passes through the stomach and is stored in a bulge in the intestine located just behind the stomach. Here the vital exchange of gases takes place, and finally the "bad" air is voided through the fish's vent.

Around the mouth of the weather fish are five pairs of small barbels, giving it the appearance of having quite a moustache. These are undoubtedly used in feeding, since the fish grubs around a good deal and also takes in quantities of disintegrated matter, apparently sifting out tiny edible particles. In the spring thousands of small, adhesive eggs are laid, usually at night.

The Neon Tetra, *Hyphessobrycon innesi,* created a sensation among tropical fish fanciers when it was introduced into Europe and the United States in 1936. The first specimen to reach the United States arrived from France on the airship *Graf Zeppelin,* and cost several hundred dollars. Neon tetras had been discovered far up the Amazon in the region where Brazil and Peru meet, and after many difficulties a few specimens were finally brought out alive. Today large shipments of them are regularly made from Brazil to the United States, and they are now one of the standard items in the large business of importing tropical freshwater fishes for home aquaria.

Few freshwater fishes can rival the neon tetra for sheer brilliance of colour; the fish really lives up to the name of "living jewel". It is a small species, mature specimens being about one and one-half inches long. Its general body colour is a neutral light grey, but the lower part of the rear of the body and base of the tail are coloured bright red, and running along each side, from the eye almost to the tail, is an iridescent blue-green band, so brilliant that it seems to arise from some electrical apparatus or molten metal rather than living tissue.

Although neon tetras have bred in captivity a number of times, they do so far too seldom to supply the great demand for them among fanciers of tropical fish, and so must be imported regularly. During spawning a pair swims through aquatic plants, the female scattering two to fifteen small, slightly adhesive eggs that may or may not become attached to the vegetation. This process is repeated at frequent intervals until perhaps two hundred eggs have been laid—a matter of two to three hours. The eggs hatch in about two days. The fry are minute, almost transparent creatures that hide among plants or hang motionless at the surface of the water.

The Blind Cave Characin, *Anoptichthys jordani,* comes from a single, small cave in the state of San Luis Potosi, Mexico—and nowhere else. In captivity, on the other hand, it is common all over the United States, in Europe, and elsewhere. This is because it has become one of the popular small "tropical fishes" of home aquarists. It is safe to say that there are many more blind cave characins living in aquaria far from their native dwelling place than exist in the Mexican cave.

Even though the cave characin is blind, its eyes being reduced to a pair of degenerate capsules more or less buried under the skin, it can hold its own in a tankful of other tropical fish in full possession of all their faculties. Although it may bump into plants, rocks, and other tank accessories when first placed in an aquarium, it very soon learns to avoid these obstacles and will swim directly towards one, unerringly turning away from it just before striking it. If you change the location of an object, the fish must learn again where it is.

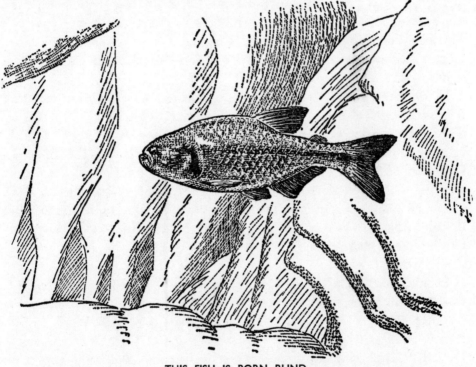

THIS FISH IS BORN BLIND

The blind cave characin is a popular fish in the home aquarium. It comes from only one place—a single, small cave in the state of San Luis Potosi, Mexico—and nowhere else. However, it has been shipped to fanciers all over the United States and to Europe. Although it is actually blind, it soon learns to adjust itself among a tankful of normal fish, and does not suffer particularly because of its handicap.

Blind cave characins quickly learn about the feeding procedure in any particular tank, and never suffer from lack of food despite the fact that they must compete with eyed fish. They generally feed on the bottom, scurrying around with such energy that, if anything, they get more than their share of food. They exhibit little nicety of taste, eating practically anything. In nature their principal food consists of the droppings of the thousands of bats that inhabit their cave.

Besides having only degenerate eyes, the blind cave characin lacks the dark pigment present in the great majority of fishes. When first taken from the cave, it is pinkish white, but after being exposed to light for some time, it becomes silvery. Its ears, too, have degenerated through the ages. It does, however, possess a greater number of taste buds than does its nearest eyed relative. Living in light has no effect on its eyes whatever; many generations have been hatched and raised in the light, and the eyes of these are not a bit less degenerate than the eyes of fish that lived all their lives in the total darkness of the Mexican cave. Reproductive habits are relatively simple. The somewhat adhesive eggs drop to the bottom, and there is no parental care of any sort.

In 1940 the New York Aquarium sponsored an expedition to study the blind cave characin in its native habitat. One of the interesting discoveries made on this trip was that the blind fish were evidently interbreeding with their eyed and pigmented relative, the Mexican Characin, *Astyanax mexicanus*. A whole series of intermediate forms, showing all stages in the lack of eyes and pigment, was found. This cross has also been successfully made in small tanks. Later exploration revealed that in the same region there are four other caves also containing blind fishes, each slightly different from the other, but all closely related.

In addition to the blind fishes of San Luis Potosi there are twenty-five or more other species of blind fishes in the world, inhabiting subterranean waters in North and South America, the West Indies, Africa, Madagascar, Asia and Australia. None of them is at all closely related to the characins, belonging to several distinctly separated families of fishes. In the United States, there are two species of blind catfishes that have been taken from artesian wells in Texas, and about eight species of blind fishes, belonging to a special family of their own, the Amblyopsidae, that inhabit a number of the limestone caves in the Midwest and Midsouth.

The Piranha, *Serrasalmus nattereri*, has killed perhaps more human beings than any other fish. Although it reaches a length of only ten

[12-11]

The tetras are South American freshwater fish, and with the piranhas, hatchet fish and electric eels, make up the second main division of Ostariophysi, the "little" bone-bladders". Tetra Perez lacks the brilliant colouring of its famous cousin, the neon tetra, but constitutes a good portion of the large business of importing tropical fish for home aquaria in the United States. Tetra occasionally breed in captivity, but the supply produced is nowhere near the demand. The eggs hatch in about two days; the fry are minute, almost transparent creatures that hide among plants or hang motion-lessly at the surface of the water. *See page 1468*

[12-12]

The dozen or so varieties of catfish with their numerous species round out the order Ostariophysi. While perhaps best known as freshwater fish of warm regions, some species are sea-dwellers. The blue catfish of the Mississippi River drainage area may weigh as much as 150 pounds, and it is considered excellent eating. *See page 1475*

[12-12A]

One of the better known species is the channel catfish, which gets its name from its preference for the clear, moving water of the channel of the streams in which it lives. In many catfish, the protruding spines are connected with poison glands; the poison of a two-inch marine species is especially effective. While different species are found throughout the world, catfish are most numerous, and most highly diversified, in South America. *See page 1475* and one-half inches, it is one of the most savage of all fishes, and no creature is too large or powerful to be attacked by it.

Its short, broad jaws are each equipped with a row of strong, triangular, razor-sharp teeth that fit into one another very closely. So powerful are the jaw muscles that only the hardest ironwood or metal can resist. Ordinary fishhooks, for example, are quickly snapped in two, and fingers or toes are amputated with grisly ease. With each bite, the piranha neatly removes from its prey a piece of flesh about the size of a large olive, this being clipped off and swallowed whole with machine-gun rapidity. The fish seems to go berserk when any blood is let, madly snapping in all directions, even biting its own companions in its frenzy.

MOST DANGEROUS OF ALL FISHES

In spite of its small size, it is probable that the piranha has taken more human lives than even the deadliest of the sharks. "Caribe" ("cannibal") is the name the Spaniards gave this dangerous creature; when it tastes blood it will even attack its own kind. The piranha is a South American freshwater fish.

Large numbers of piranhas gather wherever food is available. They have been known to strip the flesh from the bones of a living one-hundred-pound capybara in less than one minute and a four-hundred-pound hog in less than ten. Horrible stories about people being literally eaten alive by these bloodthirsty fish have been fully corroborated. Wherever they are found, piranhas are generally the most feared of water creatures. Their usual food consists of other fishes, but mammals, birds, and reptiles—in fact any sizable creatures that accidentally or deliberately get into water—are frequently destroyed. Piranhas also eat fruit and can sometimes be caught on hooks baited with balls of dough.

The piranha is a rather deep-bodied, compressed fish with a blunt, bulldog-like profile—the upper part almost vertical, the lower jaw projecting beyond the upper part of the face. It is coloured silvery blue with a light red anal fin. During the spawning season, the under-parts of the male become a brilliant red. Little is known about the reproductive habits of piranhas. They have been reported as laying adhesive eggs on submerged plants and roots and constructing a shallow nest on sandy bottoms. The parents are said to attack viciously anything approaching their eggs.

There are four dangerous species of piranhas, and they inhabit South American streams that drain into the Atlantic from northern Argentina to Venezuela. Not every river harbours them, but the Amazon, Orinoco, Paraguay, Parana, and Sao Francisco Rivers all have one or two species. *Serrasalmus nattereri* is the most widely distributed of all, being found in the Guianas, Venezuela, Brazil, Paraguay, Uruguay, and northern Argentina. The largest species is *Serrasalmus piraya*; found only in the Rio Sao Francisco, it reaches a length of at least twenty inches.

The Streaked Hatchet Fish, *Carnegiella strigata*, is one of the freshwater flying fishes and is capable of travelling through the air for distances of perhaps six feet or more over the shaded forest streams and pools of the Guianas and the Amazon, where it lives. Unlike the marine flying fishes, hatchet fishes do not glide, but actually flap—or rather, vibrate—their arched pectoral fins, like wings; their flight is therefore similar to that of insects rather than aircraft. Although they will fly to escape from a fish that is pursuing them, they never fly ashore by mistake, and while they will take off toward the open water when in danger of being caught by a net, they cannot be forced to fly towards a nearby shore, no matter how much they are harassed. Perhaps this unerring knowledge or instinct of the limits of their aquatic environment is what prevents them from ever flying in the tanks in which tropical fish fanciers keep them as pets.

To operate their "wings", hatchet fishes have tremendously developed pectoral (breast) muscles attached to a very large "sternum" or breast-bone like that of birds. This structure projects forward and downward, giving the fish a chest that is semicircular in profile and triangular in cross-section, coming to a rounded, knife-thin edge. The muscles that move the pectoral fins or "wings" may constitute as much as one-quarter of the total weight of the fish; in more ordinarily shaped species they make up less than one one-hundredth.

Streaked hatchet fish reach a length of one and three-quarter inches. They feed principally on small insects floating on the water surface. They lay eggs that float. About ten different species of hatchet fishes are known, all from northern South America or Panama.

The Electric Eel, *Electrophorus electricus,* is the most powerful of all the electric fishes. At the New York Aquarium we have measured hundreds of specimens and have found that the average maximum voltage is in excess of 350; and that at maximum power, an external current of about one-half an ampere at two hundred to three hundred volts may be drawn—that is, a hundred or more watts. This is enough to knock down a horse or to stun a man, and there are records of people having been killed by the electric eel's discharges, or drowned when they fell unconscious into the water after being shocked.

One of our medium-sized eels, about three feet long, produced discharges of 650 volts. These are the greatest we have ever recorded. One single discharge from even this particular eel is not as much, electrically, as a single discharge from a medium-sized torpedo. But the electric eel can continue to discharge for long periods of time, at a rate that varies from three hundred to thirty discharges a second—whereas the torpedo quickly becomes fatigued, after not more than fifty or so discharges.

Despite its great power, the electric eel cannot operate ordinary electric appliances and incandescent lamps. This is because each discharge lasts only about two one-thousandths of a second—while it takes an incandescent lamp, for example, as long as one-fiftieth of a second to heat up enough to be visible. The electric eel generates direct current, and the front end of the fish is always positive to the rear.

Electric eels use their electricity both to obtain food and to protect themselves. They are toothless, spineless, and scaleless creatures that swallow whole the small fishes and frogs stunned by their discharges. They inhabit the Amazon, Orinoco, and other smaller river systems of northern South America, usually being found in slow-moving, rather shallow backwaters. They are sluggish, and spend much time lying quietly in the water, only moving periodically to come to the surface for a gulp of air. The roof and floor of the mouth are specially modified to enable the fish to breathe atmospheric air, and if denied access to it electric eels drown in about ten minutes.

The electric eel is not at all related to the true eels, and, although it has a long, rather thin body, it completely lacks the sinuous grace and streamlined contours of the American eel and its relatives. With the exception of an expanse of salmon red or yellowish green on the belly and throat, the electric eel is a more or less uniform dull grey. The pectoral fins are very small. There is no dorsal or caudal fin at all, but the anal extends along the whole posterior four-fifths of the fish. By undulating this long fin the fish moves about, backwards and forwards with equal ease.

Practically nothing is known about the life history of electric eels. They undoubtedly lay eggs, but exactly where or when is pretty much of a mystery. The fish apparently disappear from their normal haunts during the rainy season, presumably going into flooded swamp lands, and at the end of that season they reappear with a cloud of small eels, an inch or so long, swimming about their head. The sex of this parent, or whether both sexes take care of the young, is unknown, but at least one parent is reported to do so until the young are five or six inches long. It is not until this time that they can produce enough electricity to defend themselves or procure food. By the time an electric eel has reached a length of about three feet, it has attained its maximum voltage, and subsequent growth only slightly increases the voltage but considerably increases the amperage. Maximum length is about nine and one-half feet.

The vital organs of the electric eel are confined to the first fifth of its length, all the rest being tail. Almost two-thirds of the tail is composed of the electric organs. These are made up of electric tissue which operates in essentially the same fashion as nerve tissue, and for this reason the electric eel has become very important in physiological and medical research.

Although sensitive to electricity, the electric eel is not harmed by its own discharges or those of its fellows. On the contrary, when an individual discharges, all others in the vicinity gather about the spot, apparently searching for food. The only "harm" done by these powerful currents seems to be the formation of opaque spots on the lenses of the eyes. All but the smallest electric eels have these, a circumstance suggesting that electric eels are apparently dependent on their own

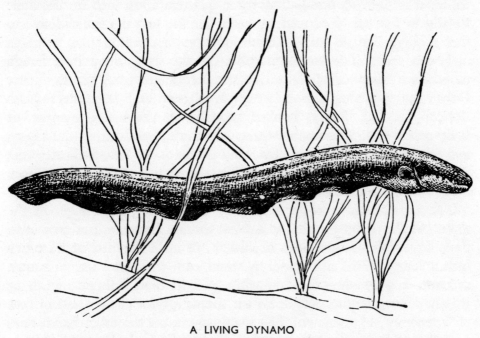

A LIVING DYNAMO

The electric eel is capable of producing more electric discharges than any other electric fish, including the torpedo; the voltage easily paralyses or kills small fish and frogs, and is sufficient to stun a man. As a result, this fish is greatly feared by the Indians of the Orinoco and Amazon, where it is found. The electric eel is a slow-moving creature and devoid of teeth—without its charge it would be hard put to defend itself or to find food.

electric discharges, operating as a sort of radar, to explore their surroundings. Whenever an electric eel moves about, it produces a series of low-powered discharges, and these are used to locate objects in its environment. At least one other species of gymnotid eel also produces small electrical discharges for the same reason; the Electric Mormyrid, *Gymnarchus niloticus*, does so in a similar manner.

The Sea Catfish, *Galeichthys felis*, carries its eggs and young in its mouth for about two months, during which time it does not eat. Only the males play the role of living incubator, and they have been reported as becoming rather scrawny toward the end of their long period of fasting. While the eggs, and later the young fish, are being carried about, the male's mouth becomes quite enlarged, and even then it sometimes seems as if he could hardly hold his offspring in—so great is their bulk.

The eggs of the sea catfish are among the largest of all the bony fishes, ranging from one-half to three-quarters of an inch in diameter. Relatively few are produced by each female, but the indications are that a single female can produce more in one season than a single male can carry. The largest number of eggs ever found in a male's mouth was forty-eight; the usual number ranges from ten to thirty. Before the spawning season, which is in June and July, the females develop peculiar, fleshy, hooked growths on the inside margins of their pelvic fins. Presumably these hooks are used during the laying and fertilization of the eggs, for what evidence we have indicates that the eggs are in some way transferred to the mouth of the male without ever touching the bottom.

The eggs hatch in about a month. The young fish remain in the mouth of the father for almost another month, however, not only until their large yolk sac has been absorbed but until they are at least two inches long. While still under parental care they feed on their own account, but whether they do while still in their father's mouth or whether they venture outside to eat, returning for shelter and in case of emergency, is unknown. The male parent, on the other hand, does not eat at all during the whole period. Most of the stomachs of incubating males that have been examined were completely empty; a few had an egg or two in them.

Sea catfish inhabit shallow brackish and salt water bays during the spring, summer and autumn. During the winter they apparently go into deeper water. This is a common species along the coast of the Gulf of Mexico, becoming rarer as one proceeds north; a specimen is found occasionally as far north as Cape Cod. The sea catfish occurs as far south as Yucatan.

The food of the sea catfish is most variable and may include crabs, shrimps, a number of other invertebrates, fishes, algae and various sea-grasses, and garbage. The species grows to a length of slightly more than sixteen and one-half inches, but males less than half that length have been found carrying eggs. The under-side of the skull of the sea catfish, and that of many of its ocean- and inlet-dwelling relatives, has two rounded, long prominences arranged more or less at right angles to each other. These are often considered to represent Jesus of Nazareth on the Cross, and the skulls are used as icons in some parts of Latin America. The fish is therefore called the "crucifix fish".

The Brown Bullhead, *Ameiurus nebulosus*, inhabits shallow, quiet, fresh waters in the eastern part of North America, from Manitoba to New Brunswick in the north, to Texas and Florida in the south. It has been introduced along the west coast and now thrives in California, Oregon, Washington, and British Columbia. It is now also found in parts of western Europe and on several of the Hawaiian Islands. The brown bullhead is remarkably hardy, being able to exist in waters too foul for practically all other fishes. It can also live for weeks at a time down in the mud, when the water of its lake, pond, or stream dries up.

The most prominent feature of the brown bullhead is the four pairs of long barbels or "whiskers" located on the chin and between the eyes and mouth. These are used to explore its surroundings, the bullhead apparently depending on them more than on its eyes. The body is without scales. There is a single stout spine in the dorsal fin and in each pectoral fin; it is these that cause the unpleasant pricks that result when the fish is not handled properly. There are no poison glands associated with the spines of the brown bullhead.

Although looked down on by many fishermen, the brown bullhead has provided many anglers with pleasure, and a great many people with cheap yet tasty and nourishing food. It takes the hook most readily, and its flesh is firm, white, sweet, and relatively boneless. The usual length is less than one foot, but specimens half as long again are known.

The food of the brown bullhead is quite varied; this fish apparently eats whatever is most available. Insect larvae and adults, crustaceans, molluscs, fishes, frogs, leeches, and worms are all taken. Plant material may be consumed in quantity, and at times fish eggs or garbage may be the chief item in its diet.

Brown bullheads prepare a nest for their eggs. This is usually in some cavity under rocks, roots, or logs, or within an abandoned muskrat hole; even objects like old tin pails may be used. Occasionally a shallow, dish-shaped nest is dug more or less out in the open. A large number of cream-coloured eggs about one-eighth of an inch in diameter are laid. There may be more than two thousand of them and they adhere to one another, forming one or more clumps. Either the male alone or both parents together may care for the eggs and young. The eggs are vigorously shaken by the fish's pelvic fins, and are taken into the mouth, "chewed" and then spat out. Hatching may occur in less than a day or may take as long as ten days. Young bullheads move about together in a school, forming a dense, black cloud of tiny fish over which the attending parent or parents will keep watch.

The Stonecat, *Noturus flavus*, the madtoms, and a number of tropical species of catfishes, unlike the brown bullhead, have poison glands in their spines and can inflict very painful and slow-healing wounds.

The Electric Catfish, *Malapterurus electricus*, has been known since ancient times. The fish was familiar to the Egyptians and also to the Greeks and Romans, and Arab writers during the Middle Ages told of its use as a love charm and as a therapeutic shocking-machine. It was first scientifically described in 1789 and imported alive into Europe in 1880; yet even today very little is known about its life history or the exact way its organs work.

Electric catfish are found through most of the western and central parts of tropical Africa and along the River Nile. They grow to a length of about four feet. They have a cylindrical body, brownish or greyish in colour, with no scales and only a very small, adipose (fatty) dorsal fin located near the tail. Surrounding the mouth are three pairs of long "whiskers". It is perhaps significant that the electric catfish, which is well able to defend itself by means of electric shocks, completely lacks the spines or armour so common among most other species of catfishes.

Little is known of the mode of life of the electric catfish save that it inhabits rivers and swamps. It is reported as eating algae, worms, and fish, but its exact diet in nature has apparently never been recorded. In captivity is cannot be kept with other members of its species; in any tank, one and only one electric catfish survives. Nothing is known of its reproductive habits.

There is no doubt that the strong electric shocks which the electric catfish is capable of producing are used defensively, but whether they are also employed offensively, that is, to stun prey, is still a question. What reports there are on the strength of the electric discharges of the fish appear quite different from one another. We have measured a number of specimens ranging from about four to eight inches in length and have found their maximum discharge to run at about eighty volts. The electric organ consists of a special, gelatinous coat of tissue that covers most of the body just under the skin.

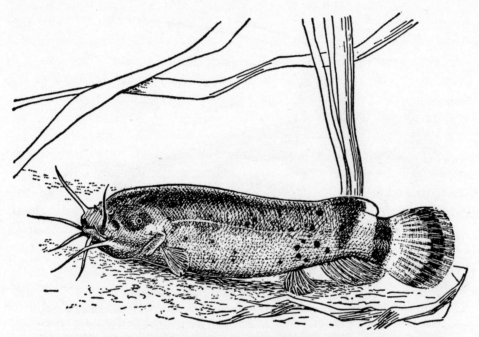

CATFISH WITH AN ELECTRIC CHARGE

The "bewhiskered" creatures called catfish are well known to fishermen in Europe, America, and Australia; less familiar is the electric catfish of Africa. An eight-inch individual is capable of producing a charge of eighty volts. In earlier times the electric catfish is said to have been used in the treatment of epilepsy.

The Whiptail Loricaria, *Loricaria parva,* at first glance looks like a living fossil, a creature out of the dim past, when all fishes were flattened and heavily armoured. The truth of the matter is, however, that the family of armoured catfishes to which the whiptail loricaria belongs is among the most specialized or "modern" of all the catfishes, and that it consists not of a few relics, but of a flourishing group of more than four hundred different species, inhabiting almost all the fresh waters of tropical South and Central America.

The whiptail loricaria reaches a length of about eight inches. It has a depressed head that is semi-circular in outline and shield-shaped, followed by a roughly triangular body that tapers to a long whisk of a tail, terminating in a small fin with a long ray, or whip, at its upper edge. The whole fish is covered with bony armour, the head and fore-part of the body being sheathed in an inflexible case, and the rest of the fish in movable, overlapping plates. The colour is greyish brown with darker transverse bands and blotches.

A CATFISH WITH A COAT OF ARMOUR

The whiptail loricaria belongs to the family of armoured catfish. With its flattened, heavily armoured body it looks like a fish of ancient times but it is really a thoroughly "up-to-date" modern fish. Here a male rests on a batch of eggs, guarding them and keeping them clean with his mouth.

Like other armoured catfishes, the whiptail loricaria spends most of its time on or near the bottom and is most active during the hours of twilight and darkness. It feeds on organic matter which it sucks up from the bottom, on algae scraped from rocks, or on plants. Its sucker-like mouth is located on the under-side of the head. The mouth is often employed to hold the fish in place—for example, on the vertical side of a stone or the glass walls of an aquarium. Many armoured cat-fishes live in swift-flowing streams and use their mouths to keep from being washed downstream by the current. At least one species is able to inch up high waterfalls, in spite of the strong flow of water, by means of its sucking mouth.

In preparation for spawning a pair of whiptail loricaria clean off a rock or bit of hard bottom. The forty or so large, amber eggs are carefully cared for by the male who rests directly upon them, cleaning them with his mouth and fanning them with his large pectoral fins. After eight to ten days, the eggs hatch into baby fish about three-eighths of an inch long. The father shows no interest in his offspring, however.

Whiptail loricaria are native to fresh waters in Paraguay and southern Brazil.

The Eels—Fishes like Snakes

AN EEL is just an eel to the person who does not know the fishes of this group well. But once you start to examine them closely, you will find many remarkable contrasts among them. Some are large, brightly coloured, savage animals whose bite may be poisonous—at the other extreme are tiny, inoffensive, burrowing creatures that look and behave like worms. Even these are interesting: you would be astonished at the rapidity with which they can dig themselves into the sand or mud, tail first.

As recently as seventy-five years ago, the life story of the eels was one of the great riddles of nature. Up to that time, no one knew how they bore their young or what stages they passed through. The ancients thought these curious snakelike fishes arose through spontaneous generation from "the bowels of the earth" or the morning dew, or came from horsehairs that fell into water or from small beetles or the gills of other fishes.

So far as we now know, all eels lay their eggs in salt water. The young pass through a flat, transparent stage, at which time they hardly look like eels at all. Most species remain in the sea all their lives, but some live for long periods in fresh water, returning to the sea to lay their eggs.

The eels are very long, have tiny scales or none at all. They lack spines in their fins and have a characteristic kind of upper jaw. None of them possesses pelvic fins; some also are without pectorals, and a few have no fins whatsoever. The giants of the group (order Apodes, meaning "footless") range in length up to ten feet and in weight to more than one hundred pounds. Among the twenty or so families are the common edible eels of Europe and eastern North America and their relatives (Anguillidae), the conger eels (Leptocephalidae), and the moray eels (Muraenidae).

The fishes of this order might be called the "true eels", although sometimes we reserve that term for members of the family Anguillidae. At any rate, a number of wholly unrelated fishes are termed eels, among them the slime-eels and lamprey eels, the gymnotid eels or knifefishes, the synbranchid or swamp-eels, the mastacembelid or spiny eels, the cusk-eels and the rock-eel. Except for the long, supple body, these fishes have little in common.

The American Eel, *Anguilla rostrata*, was for many years a mystery fish. Although it was well known in the lakes, ponds, and streams of eastern North and Central America and of Bermuda and the West Indies, its life history puzzled scientists and laymen alike. No one knew where or when this important foodfish spawned; no one had ever seen the egg or young of the eel. When, after years of patient, careful work, the life cycles of both the American eel and its European cousin were revealed, for sheer strangeness and fascination they exceeded all expectations.

Mature female American eels, one and one-half to six feet long and about seven to twelve years old, migrate to the coast, entering the sea in the autumn. To accomplish this they must sometimes travel overland, which they probably do at night, and while out of water they breathe through their skin. Mature males do not have to travel so far, since they grow up near the coast in brackish water. (They are usually smaller than the females, ranging from about twelve to eighteen inches in length.)

The goal of the eels' journey is an area in the Atlantic Ocean a few hundred miles south-west of Bermuda, in and around the Sargasso Sea. Here in midwinter they spawn and then die.

The young eels are tiny, flattened, transparent creatures that do not remotely resemble eels—we call them leptocephalus larvae. They slowly make their way back towards the continent and arrive on the eastern coast in the spring less than a year and a half after they were spawned. By this time they have assumed an eel-shaped but transparent form. They are a little over two inches long. Soon they begin to darken, and those destined to be females start their long migration up streams. Now they are called elvers.

The European Eel, *Anguilla anguilla*, has a similar life history, but takes three years to change from a leptocephalus larva into elver. In all, there are sixteen different species of eels that are closely related to the European and American ones. They are found throughout most of the warm temperate and tropical seas, with the exception of the eastern Pacific. There are none of these eels on the Pacific coast of the United States.

Under certain conditions, in captivity for example, eels never mature, and have lived for as long as fifty-six years without showing signs of becoming reproductive adults.

The Conger Eel, *Conger oceanicus,* looks like the American eel in a general way. But we can quickly recognize the conger eel by its dorsal fin, which rises just above and behind the small pair of pectorals. In the American eel this fin begins a long way back from the pectorals. Moreover, the American eel has minute scales embedded in its skin: the conger eel has no scales whatsoever.

The life history of these two species is also somewhat different. Conger eels spend all of their lives in salt water and only make a relatively short migration offshore into deeper waters to spawn. The tiny eggs float, and the young fish go through a leptocephalus stage before becoming eel-shaped. At this stage they are very small, flattened, transparent creatures, so unlike their parents that for a long time they were thought to be a different kind of fish. Not until 1886—when some leptocephalus larvae were kept in captivity while they underwent their remarkable transformation into small conger eels—was their true identity demonstrated.

The conger eel is widely distributed on both sides of the Atlantic, but does not occur on the west coast of the United States. Those from Europe are generally considerably larger than those found off the shores of the United States, where specimens over four feet long are unusual.

These are females, males attaining about two and one-half feet. The largest conger eel on record weighed 128 pounds and was about eight feet long.

The Green Moray, *Gymnothorax funebris*, is as ferocious as it looks. It has a powerful, sinuous body that may be six or more feet long, and strong jaws armed with many sharp teeth. Although sometimes used for food, it is greatly feared by West Indian and Bermudian fishermen and divers who come into contact with it.

Its solid green colour results from a layer of bright yellow slime that covers its slate-blue, tough, scaleless skin. Other morays, of which there are over a hundred, are marked with all sorts of stripes, bars, spots, and blotches. They can be distinguished from other kinds of eels by the lack of pectoral and pelvic fins and their small, round gill openings.

Morays inhabit coral reefs as a rule, and in captivity seem most contented when they can squeeze themselves into some hole or crevice. They retain their savage dispositions in the aquarium; tankmen never become familiar with them even though morays sometimes learn to feed from the hand.

Killies, Guppies, and Their Relatives —Small but Useful

THE KILLIES, guppies, and their relatives compose a colourful group. All are small, but man has found a use for them. Some are valuable research animals, others help prevent the breeding of mosquitoes, and a few are famous as household pets—inside glass, of course.

There are more than five hundred species in this group (order Cyprinodontes, a name meaning "toothed carp"). Most of them inhabit fresh water, but we find a small number in brackish or salt waters. The largest of any of them is about one foot. They lack spines in the fins, and the poor development or absence of the lateral line on the body (although it is well developed on the head) is noteworthy. The best-known families are: the North American cavefishes (Amblyopsidae); the egg-laying topminnows or killifishes (Cyprinodontidae); the live-bearing topminnows (Poeciliidae); and the four-eye fishes (Anablepidae).

We know about eight species of North American cavefishes. With one or two exceptions they are small pink and white fishes without eyes, that inhabit cold, limestone caves in the central part of the United States. The two hundred or so egg-laying topminnows are found in every continent except Australia and include such interesting creatures as the mummichog and the desert minnows, together with a number of popular, colourful home-aquarium fishes. The well-known guppy, and the platyfishes, swordtails, and mollies belong among the live-bearing topminnows. This family was originally found only in North, South, and Central America and the West Indies, but several of its members have been deliberately or accidentally introduced into many other parts of the world.

The Mummichog, or Killie, *Fundulus heteroclitus,* can live in polluted and diluted sea water that would quickly be fatal to most salt-water fishes. Although primarily a salt-water fish, it often goes into brackish and fresh waters of its own free will, especially in the spring. It can also withstand drastic changes in temperature and can live out of water for a considerable time.

As might be expected with so adaptable an animal, the mummichog is very common and occurs in large numbers throughout the greater part of its range, from the Gulf of St. Lawrence to Texas, It is a shallow-water fish but is sometimes supposed to go into deeper water offshore during the winter. The toughness and availability of the mummichog have made it a favourite laboratory animal, both for experiments and teaching. Hundreds of scientific papers about it have already been published, and more are written each year. The mummichog has aided man in other ways, too, namely, as a bait fish and as a destroyer of salt-marsh mosquitoes.

Mummichogs are killifish and belong to a large group of fishes called topminnows because as a rule they live just under the water's surface. Their mouths equip them to feed at the surface, the lower jaw being extended and the upper jaw foreshortened so that the mouth opens practically at a level with the top of the head. A wide variety of food, both plant and animal and both living and dead, is consumed by the mummichog. Maximum size is from five to six inches, the females being slightly larger on the average than the males.

The male mummichog is more brightly coloured than the female, and during the breeding season, which is early spring to late summer depending on the latitude, his colours become especially bright. It has been shown by experiments that this type of colour is strongly influenced by male hormones (internal secretions produced by the testes). At breeding time the males pursue the females ardently and fight fiercely with one another. The sticky eggs are laid on the bottom or on stones or plants. They hatch in from nine to eighteen days, and the young are further advanced in development than are most baby fishes just hatched from the egg.

The Desert Minnow, *Cyprinodon macularius*, is one of a number of fishes that live in the creeks, springs, and waterholes of American deserts. Like several of them, the desert minnow is able to withstand high temperatures that would rapidly kill the great majority of fishes. Desert minnows have been found in natural waters that reach 100° Fahrenheit and have lived comfortably in captivity at 102 degrees. (This is the temperature of a warm bath.) The highest temperature at which an American fish has definitely been found living in nature is 104 degrees, in a hot spring near Death Valley, and the fish involved is a close relative of the desert minnow.

Strangely enough, the desert minnow can also withstand low temperatures, nearly down to freezing in certain circumstances. It is also quite tolerant of changes in the amount of salt and other dissolved chemicals in the water surrounding it. It can live in water that is either fresh or quite heavily charged with chemicals.

The desert minnow is found throughout a large part of the southwestern United States, the state of Sonora in Mexico, and Baja California. Adults are about two inches long. Males are a pale blue colour that is especially bright during breeding. Females are brownish and more slender than males. The males are pugnacious during breeding; they fight lustily with one another at this time. The adhesive eggs are laid

A FAMOUS GAMEFISH FIGHTS CAPTURE

The tarpon with its coarse, somewhat bitter flesh does not share the commercial importance of its close relative, the herring, as a foodfish, but the handsome, silvery creature attracts sportsmen because of its fighting qualities and leaping powers. While the average tarpon weighs about 65 pounds, one of the largest taken with tackle weighed 247 pounds and was $7\frac{1}{2}$ feet long. Primarily inhabitants of the tropical Atlantic Ocean, tarpon frequently venture up the rivers to fresh water. A smaller species lives in the Indian and Wĕstern Pacific Oceans, and it, too, often enters rivers and lives for considerable lengths of time in fresh water. *See page 1433.*

A FISH WITH REMARKABLE EYES

This strange-looking creature with the bulging eyes is known as the foureye fish (why it is so named is explained below). It is found in some of the warmer waters of the New World, and is so agile that it is not easily caught. Small crustaceans, insects, and algae make up its diet.
See page 1492.

THE FOUREYE FISH CRUISES ALONG THE SURFACE

The upper half of the eye of the foureye fish is adapted for vision in air above the water-line, while the lower half is adjusted in seeing in the water. A dumbbell-shaped pupil makes simultaneous use of these parts possible. The fish spends most of its time at or close to the surface.
See page 1492.

singly or in clusters, and stick to the bottom or to plants. Young desert minnows grow very rapidly and become mature in less than four months. There is evidence that the fish breeds all the year round in some of the warm springs it inhabits.

The Guppy, *Lebistes reticulatus,* has introduced more people to the problems and satisfactions of keeping tropical fishes as pets than any other member of that group of small, warm freshwater species now maintained in home aquaria all over the world. Its bright colours, incessant activity, interesting reproductive habits, and, above all, its extreme hardiness have made it one of the most popular and best known of all fishes.

Scientists, too, appreciate some of these characteristics, and guppies have been employed in studies and experiments for the past thirty years with ever-increasing frequency. The guppy has proved beneficial in still another way. In fact the first use to which the fish was put was to aid in the control of the mosquitoes carrying that world-wide scourge, malaria—by eating up their aquatic larvae.

Originally found in the streams, ponds, ditches, and the brackish, coastal waters of northern South America, Trinidad, Antigua, Barbados, and the Windward Islands as far north as St. Lucia, the guppy has now been transplanted to many parts of the tropical world, including such widely separated localities as Ceylon, Singapore, Borneo, Tahiti, the Hawaiian Islands, and Argentina. Not all the introductions were for the purpose of mosquito control, however. A few were accidental, the fish escaping from captivity in garden pools. Others were made by fish fanciers simply "for the fun of it"—a very dangerous practice, since foreign animals can become veritable plagues: witness the rabbit in Australia and the carp in the United States. Fortunately, the guppy does not seem to have become a pest in any of those widespread places in which it has become established, except on the island of Mauritius, where it is said to be very destructive to the eggs of certain edible fishes and crayfishes.

So numerous in parts of its original home that it is called the "millions fish", the guppy is apparently as successful in the wild as it is in captivity. It feeds on a variety of small foods such as adult and larval insects, the eggs of other fishes, and algae. In turn, the guppy is preyed upon by a number of larger fishes and by some birds.

In Nature male guppies rarely exceed three-quarters of an inch, while females regularly grow to twice that length. Males are coloured with patches of pastel reds, oranges, yellows, greens, and violets and with a few black spots. So various are their colour patterns that no two seem exactly alike.

Fanciers have taken advantage of this great natural variability to create dozens of differently coloured strains by selective breeding. Experiments have shown that these masculine colours are under the influence both of the heredity and the hormones of the fish; they are inherited, but need the presence of the male hormone for full development. Female guppies have deeper bodies than males and lack their bright colours. In captivity, however, some strains that have malelike coloration have been developed through selective breeding. Fancy strains of albino guppies, golden guppies, and guppies with peculiarly shaped tails are also now established.

Guppies are viviparous, that is, they bring forth their young alive. Under the best of conditions, females can have their first brood in less than three months. First broods are quite small in number, but the female continues to grow after reaching maturity, and for this reason and others, her broods become larger, too. The average maximum number of young born at one time is in the neighbourhood of fifty, but broods as large as 126 have been reported. The minimum time between broods is twenty-three days but usually twenty-eight or more days elapse. The young are nurtured within the female's ovary, not the uterus as in mammals; but it has been shown that, like the mammal, the mother fish contributes nourishment to her developing offspring. Fertilization is effected by means of the gonopodium, the modified anal fin of the male.

Male guppies seem to be ardent gallants, for they court the females almost incessantly. The latter seldom take any heed of their antics, however, save to flee from the attentions of some too-persistent suitor. Females have had as many as eight broods after being isolated from all other fish. This is made possible by the ability to store the male sexual element for many months.

Guppies live to be about three years old. In Nature, and captivity too, young are born the year round, although reproductive activities are usually more intense at some seasons of the year than at others.

The guppy was first imported alive into Germany in 1908. At that time, its correct scientific name was generally thought to be *Girardinus guppyi*. This name had been proposed in honour of Dr. Robert

Lechmere Guppy, a scientist who lived in Trinidad. Some five years later it was definitely shown that, according to the international rules of scientific nomenclature, the fish's correct name was *Lebistes reticulatus*, but by the time this fact became known, the popular name, guppy, had become too well established to be changed.

The Mosquito Fish, *Gambusia affinis*, has been transplanted into more than seventy different countries to help man in his never-ending battle against the mosquitoes, especially those that transmit malaria.

Originally found in north-eastern Mexico and much of the south-eastern United States—as far north as southern Illinois and New Jersey—this small fish, since 1905, has been introduced into every continent except Australia. It has become a tenant of such far-flung islands as Cyprus, Ceylon, Guadalcanal, Samoa, Tahiti, Hawaii, the Marianas, Fijis, Philippines, Carolines, Ryukyus, and Celebes. Within the United States, the fish has been carried to the West Coast, and a cold-resistant strain has become established as far north as Chicago.

The mosquito fish is now the most widely distributed freshwater fish in the world.

Although mosquito fish do not totally eliminate mosquitoes that breed in the water they inhabit, they have been found highly efficient in keeping the number of those pests quite low. One captive adult female was seen to consume more than 150 mosquito larvae in the course of ten hours. Such gluttony would undoubtedly be rare under most natural conditions, but the observation gives an idea of the ravenous appetites exhibited by these small fish.

Female mosquito fish occasionally reach a length of two and one-half inches; usually they are about one and three-quarter inches long. Males are smaller, never attaining one and one-half and rarely exceeding one and one-quarter inches. This difference in size results mostly from females continuing to grow throughout life, while males practically cease growing once they have attained adulthood. Females also live longer than males, the maximum life span in nature usually being not more than fifteen months. In any given locality there are almost always many more females than males.

In tropical regions, mosquito fish breed all the year round, but where winters are cool or cold, they breed only during the warmer months. The young are born alive, an average brood consisting of forty to fifty babies. These are about five-sixteenths of an inch long at birth, and as many as 315 young have been found inside a two-and-one-half-inch female. Females have a brood every three to four weeks but, in the north at least, have no more than four or five broods before old age sets in. All this adds up to a tremendous reproductive capacity for a live-bearing animal and helps to explain the usefulness of the mosquito fish in reducing the number of mosquitoes.

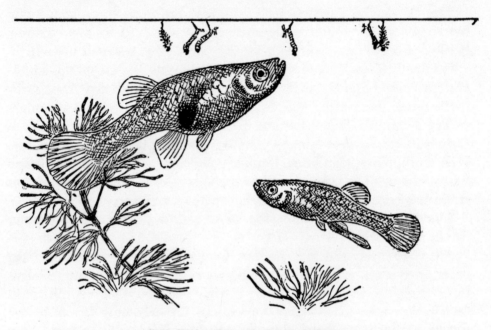

THIS FISH HELPS US FIGHT DISEASE

One of the world's greatest sanitation workers is the mosquito fish, shown here in the act of attacking mosquito larvae at the surface of the water. Thanks to the efforts of this creature, the activity of malaria-bearing mosquitoes has been sharply curtailed. Once found only in the United States, the mosquito fish has been introduced into more countries than any other freshwater fish.

Male mosquito fish are easily distinguished from females by the presence of a gonopodium, the modified anal fin used in fertilization. The development of this structure—and of other masculine characteristics too—has been shown to be dependent upon the presence of male sex hormone. As in many other live-bearing fishes, it is possible for the female mosquito fish to have several broods after a single contact with a male. As many as five successive litters have been observed in females that were isolated in small aquaria.

The food of mosquito fish does not consist solely of mosquito larvae, of course. They will eat practically any animal, provided it is small enough, and also small plants, especially algae. They are also not averse to eating their own young, both in captivity and in Nature.

The Common Platyfish, *Xiphophorus maculatus,* is endowed with a more extensive series of fixed colour patterns than any other backboned animal in North America, and perhaps in the whole world. More than 150 different colour varieties of common platyfish have been found in Nature, and, with further collecting, still more will undoubtedly be discovered. Platyfishes show several kinds of black spotting, located on many different parts of the fish's body and fins. If the three different red-pigmented patterns and the one or two blue ones—that are also found in combination with the black ones—are considered, the total number of colour varieties would be several times 150.

Except for this extreme variability of colour pattern, the common platyfish is not a fish of striking appearance. It grows to a length of a little more than two inches, females being slightly larger than males. A male can be easily distinguished from a female by his gonopodium, which is the anal fin modified into a sticklike organ used in fertilization.

The female common platyfish gives birth to living young. At the height of her reproductive capacity she has a brood every twenty-eight days. The period of gestation is only twenty-one days, however, for the new brood does not start to develop until a week after the preceding one has been born. At birth, baby platyfish are a little less than a quarter of an inch long. They are able to swim and immediately seek shelter among floating plants at the top of the water if these are available. The largest brood on record is that of a wild-caught female who had 168 babies just ready to be liberated.

Common platyfish inhabit lowland fresh waters of the Atlantic drainage in British Honduras, Guatemala, and southern Mexico, excluding Yucatan. They prefer slow-moving, weedy waters, but have been found in a number of different types of streams, lakes, ponds, ditches, and temporary pools. They feed on both small animals and plants.

Tropical-fish fanciers are well acquainted with the common platyfish. Since 1907, when the first living specimens were imported into Germany, they have been one of the hobby's favourites. Fish breeders have developed a number of colourful strains, including blue, gold, black, and red ones. One popular strain, the wagtail, was originated at the New York Aquarium. In this, the rays of all the fins are heavily pigmented, giving to them a black, lacelike effect.

The Mexican Swordtail, *Xiphophorus helleri*, is a close relative of the common platyfish. It, too, is a popular fish with home aquarists and was first imported alive into Germany in 1909, two years after the platyfish. One of the first things the German aquarists discovered was that the swordtail and platyfish could be cross-bred. From these crosses a number of beautifully coloured hybrids developed. For example, all of the red platies and swordtails we commonly see in pet shops and home aquaria are hybrids; one may have to go back many generations, however, to discover the original cross.

It is a strange fact that although the common platyfish and the swordtail are frequently found in the same ponds and streams of Mexico, they never hybridize in nature. Apparently they will only cross-breed in the confines of an aquarium.

The outstanding feature of the Mexican swordtail is the "sword" which is carried by the males. This is a long, pointed extension of the lower part of the tail fin. The largest swordtail males are more than six inches long and about half of this length is made up of sword. To what use the fish puts its sword is not known. It has been suggested that the sword is displayed during courtship, but whether it actually excites or entices the female is questionable.

Swordtails are found in the Atlantic drainage of Honduras, British Honduras, Guatemala, and Southern Mexico, excluding Yucatan. They seem to prefer higher, cooler waters than the common platyfish, although the two species, as mentioned before, often live together.

Certain kinds of platyfish-swordtail hybrids regularly fall victim to black cancer, called "melanoma", and they have therefore been used in medical research on this disease. In the Genetics Laboratory of the New York Aquarium, located in the American Museum of Natural History, there are hundreds of tanks containing special strains of different kinds of platyfishes and swordtails that are being studied and experimented with in many ways. These fishes are fast becoming aquatic counterparts of the white rat and guinea pig.

The Foureye Fish, *Anableps anableps*, which cruises at the surface, has eyes so wonderfully constructed that it can see above and below water at the same time. The pupil of the eye is actually dumb-bell-shaped, and the fish swims with the upper part out of water and the lower part submerged. This arrangement and the difference in curvature of the corresponding parts of the lens are such that objects both above and below the surface of the water are focused on different regions of the retina at the same time. Thus, foureye fish can be aware of what is going on in two elements at once.

The fish seem very alert, too, for they are among the most difficult of all fishes to catch. At the slightest disturbance or movement on shore, foureye fish skitter away. They appear to know exactly how a net works, and more often than not whole schools will escape capture by hurdling the top. Nor will they take the fly or be fished for in any other manner. Some fishermen capture them with cast-nets at night, at which time they can be blinded by torches, and museum collectors have resorted to shooting them with scatter-shot. Despite the difficulties of capture, foureye fish are sold for food in some South American markets. They reach a length of about one foot.

Foureye fish inhabit fresh or brackish waters in streams, lakes, and tidal flats. Their somewhat elongated, cylindrical bodies are flattened on top, and as they swim at the surface, only their eyes project out of the water, these being elevated as in a frog. The fish feed on algae and on insect adults and larvae and small crustaceans, found at or near the water surface. Foureye fish are born alive. They are one and three-quarter inches long at birth, and a nine-inch female may have from six to thirteen in a single brood. The female's ovary, in which the eggs are produced and the young nurtured, contains an elaborate apparatus for the nourishment of the developing offspring.

This species of foureye fish is found in northern South America along the Atlantic drainage and in Trinidad. There are two other species, one from South America and the other from southern Mexico and much of Central America.

Needle Fishes, Flying Fishes, and Halfbeaks

FISHES of this group are fascinating natural entertainers. Needle fishes skitter about the surface of the water like living javelins; halfbeaks are flip-flop artists and wrestlers; and flying fishes are aquatic aviators. They live mostly at the surface of tropical and warm temperate seas, and range in length from about one inch to five feet.

Some fifty needle fishes or marine gars—thin but savage hunters—comprise the family Belonidae. From sixty to seventy-five different halfbeaks (family Hemirhamphidae) have also been accounted for. Several members of both these groups enter streams and lakes occasionally, and others do so regularly.

In certain lakes and streams of south-eastern Asia, the East Indies, and the Philippines, there are small halfbeaks that never live in the sea. Unlike other members of the order, some of these give birth to living young. The Siamese selectively breed one of them, *Dermogenys pusillus*, for combat, as they do the better-known Siamese fighting fish. These tiny halfbeak males fight by grasping each other with their jaws and wrestling, sometimes for hours at a time. The family Exocoetidae is made up of the flying fishes, of which there are about sixty species.

The fishes of this order have curious jaws, to which they owe their scientific name (Synentognathi—it means "with inner jaws"). You can recognize them by the lack of spines in the fins and by the high attachment of the pectoral fins. The dorsal and pelvic fins are located to the rear and the lateral line has a low position.

The Atlantic Needle Fish, *Strongylura marina*, lives at the surface of waters along the east coast of the United States, from Maine to Texas, and it seems admirably equipped for the predatory life it leads. Its silvery body is cylindrical and extremely thin; a specimen six inches long is scarcely bigger around than a lead pencil. About one-fifth of its total length is occupied by its jaws, which are prolonged into a narrow, bill-like structure and lined their whole length with numerous sharply pointed teeth. It preys almost exclusively on small fish. The needle fish usually catches its victim crosswise between its jaws, artfully juggles the hapless fish about until it faces the mouth, and then swallows it whole, head first. Occasionally shrimps are also caught and eaten.

The eggs of the Atlantic needle fish are provided with tufts of long tendrils, which entangle the eggs with any object they touch. Development apparently takes an unusually long time even at high temperatures. So far as known, these fish reproduce during the summer. For a while, the lower jaw of the young needle fish is much longer than the upper one; not until it reaches a total length of at least six inches does its upper jaw approach the lower one in size. Atlantic needle fish four feet long are on record, although very few exceed two and one-half feet.

This species is much given to leaping and skittering over the water's surface, like a silvery javelin. It also occasionally hurdles small floating objects like sticks. Other species of needle fishes indulge in this peculiar behaviour quite frequently, jumping again and again over a floating straw, twig, stick, leaf, feather, or piece of paper. No completely satisfactory explanation of these antics has yet been forthcoming. In certain instances it seems as if the fish are trying to scrape tiny parasites off their bodies. Another possible explanation is that they are playing. but no one knows just what "animal play" is, especially among fishes.

Like a good number of other needle fishes, the Atlantic species travels up streams and can be seen living in fresh water.

The Halfbeak, *Hyporhamphus unifasciatus,* seems actually to possess half a beak! It has a short upper jaw, only about one-half an inch long in the largest specimens, but its lower jaw is much longer, being eight or more times the length of the upper one. There are no teeth on the projecting jaw, nor does it ever seem to be used as a spear or broadsword. When food is seized by the halfbeak, the upper, not the lower, jaw is moved. In the present fragmentary state of our knowledge about these fishes, the exact function of this peculiar structure remains a matter of guesswork.

Halfbeaks feed on small crustaceans, molluscs, and on vegetable matter, mostly algae. They spawn in the summer, laying semi-buoyant eggs. Very small individuals have no beak, but when they are slightly longer than half an inch the lower jaw begins to elongate. A maximum size of about one foot is attained.

This species is found from Massachusetts south through the West Indies, and it is common south of Chesapeake Bay. Like other half-beaks, it habitually lives at or near the surface. Specimens have been seen flipping themselves over small floating objects such as match boxes and bits of seaweed. The fish swims up to the object and places the tip of its lower jaw just under it. A violent flip follows, and the fish lands on the other side, generally facing in the opposite direction. This per-formance may be repeated half a dozen times. What it means is a mystery. Some species of halfbeaks make great leaps over the water or propel the forepart of their body out of it, sculling themselves along with their tails, which is the only part remaining in the water. This behaviour closely resembles the taxiing of their relatives, the flying fishes.

The Twowing Flying Fish, *Exocoetus volitans*, is the commonest flying fish of the Atlantic and is also found in the warm portions of the Indian and Pacific Oceans. It is a truly oceanic fish, most frequently seen in tropical mid-oceans. It reaches a length of seven inches.

This fish has greatly enlarged pectoral fins, and these constitute its wings. With them the fish can glide through the air—which it often does when disturbed by a ship or pursued by some larger fish. The twowing flying fish has no teeth and feeds upon plankton (minute plants and animals floating at or near the surface of the sea).

Ripe specimens have been taken during the first half of the year. The eggs are smooth and are pelagic—that is, they float at or near the surface of the open sea.

The Atlantic Fourwing Flying Fish, *Cypselurus heterurus*, is one of the species of flying fishes seen from ships by travellers sailing around Florida and the West Indies and in the Mediterranean. In this species both the pectoral and pelvic fins are enlarged, giving the fish two pairs of wings.

For many years it was argued whether flying fishes flapped their wings like birds or glided like aircraft. Anatomical studies have shown the former method to be an impossibility, since flying fishes completely lack the bulky muscles necessary to work flapping wings—such muscles as compose the meaty breast of a bird. Nevertheless, many observers claimed that they saw the fishes' wings move, especially during the first stages of flight.

A study of the structure of flying fish from the viewpoint of the aircraft designer has proved that their wings are sufficiently well designed to support them in gliding flight. Very careful observations in nature confirmed this and revealed just how the flying fish starts and maintains its glide; they also showed that the so-called "wing flapping" was an optical illusion created in part by the instability of the fish when taking off. Finally, stroboscopic photography, which shows the successive steps of a movement, no matter how rapid, confirmed what had been previously deduced from theory and from wind-tunnel experiments.

Swimming very rapidly in the fashion of most fish—with pectoral and pelvic fins held close to the body—the fourwing flying fish drives the front part of its body out of water into the air. It then spreads its great pectoral fins or wings, and these provide enough lift to sustain the body in the air—all except part of the tail. The lower lobe of the tail fin of flying fishes is half again as long as the upper one. With this lobe acting as a scull, the fish taxis for perhaps a hundred feet, accelerating all the while. Finally the fish spreads its pelvic fins and the added lift raises the tail out of the water. The fish now glides freely above the ocean's surface.

The usual flight of a fish of this type covers roughly fifty yards and lasts not quite three seconds. The speed of flight averages about thirty-five miles per hour, being about forty at the start and twenty-five at the finish. Much longer flights are possible, however; flights lasting thirteen seconds have been recorded with a stop watch. Like good pilots, flying fish generally take off into the wind, and it is entirely possible that they take advantage of wind currents during flight, for they have considerable manoeuvrability in air and can bank and adjust the angle of their wings.

Often the fourwing flying fish allows the lower lobe of its tail fin to drop back into the water during flight and then taxis again, regaining flying speed. Any single flight usually contains only one or two such leaps, but as many as eleven successive leaps have been observed before the fish finally dropped back into the water completely. These compound flights naturally last longer than do the simple ones. The fish may remain out of water—except for its tail fin—for half a minute or so, and may travel a quarter of a mile. Ordinarily, flying fish glide from three to six feet above the water's surface, but air currents may lift them much higher—on to the decks of ships, for example.

To end its flight a fourwing flying fish simply closes its wings and falls into the water, sometimes head first, sometimes belly first, occasionally even upside down. Flights are made both at night and in the daytime. Flying fishes seem to be attracted to lights, and a number meet untimely deaths by crashing into ships, landing on decks, and flying through portholes at night.

The Atlantic fourwing flying fish is dark above and silver below in colour. The wings, that is, the pectoral fins, are a uniform grey with a single lighter band extending obliquely outwards across them. Younger specimens have their wings quite differently marked. In fact the fish goes through a remarkable series of changes involving both colour and structure as it grows up. Among other things, the young up to a length of at least three inches have a pair of prominent barbels on the chin. All this was quite perplexing to scientists, who described the young stages under a number of different names and confused them with other species of flying fishes. A maximum length of somewhat over one foot is attained by the Atlantic fourwing flying fish.

The food of flying fish apparently consists only of small animals and plants floating in the sea. Young specimens have been seen poking around in floating seaweed and catching small creatures there. Flying fishes are themselves preyed upon by a number of different fishes, the most noteworthy being the dorado, or dolphin. Certain sea birds live almost exclusively on flying fish.

Reproduction in the Atlantic fourwing flying fish occurs during the summer. The spherical eggs, one-sixteenth of an inch in size, are attached to each other by means of numerous tendrils which run out from the surface. They are also attached to very long filaments so that they look like groups of tiny beads on somewhat tangled skeins of fine cotton thread. These filaments are found wrapped around all sorts of floating objects like seaweed, sticks, branches, cork, pumice, and the discarded straw wrappings of wine bottles. The utility of this arrangement becomes apparent when we realize that the eggs and threads are heavier than water, and if they were not buoyed up, they would sink to their death in the cold, sunless depths of the sea. The young are about a quarter of an inch long when first hatched. For some time they remain in or around their floating cradle before taking up an existence in the open sea.

The Atlantic fourwing flying fish has been found as far north as Massachusetts and Norway, but occurs in numbers only in warm waters. The thrill of unexpectedly seeing a group of these fish suddenly leave the water and gracefully sail through the air for a hundred feet or more before dropping back into the sea is a memorable one.

The California Flying Fish, *Cypselurus californicus*, grows to a length of eighteen inches and is probably the largest of all flying fishes. It occurs in schools from Point Conception south along the West Coast to Baja California. It is one of the four-winged types, and is coloured deep blue on its back and sides and silvery white on its belly. This species is one of the sights around Santa Catalina Island, where its spectacular flights are watched by numerous tourists.

FLYING FISH WITH FOUR WINGS

The California flying fish, a four-winged creature that is deep blue above and white below, may reach a length of a foot and a half. It travels in schools, and a group of these fish breaking the surface and launching themselves into the air present a spectacle that is not soon forgotten.

Flying fishes make delicious eating, but are nowhere caught in sufficient numbers to support a large fishery. They are commercially caught during certain seasons of the year, however, off Barbados, India, and the Celebes. In the last two places they are lured by bunches of leaves and twigs which the fishermen throw on the surface of the sea. The fish congregate about this floating material to lay their eggs. The California flying fish is regularly taken with gill-nets, but is not used for food to any extent. Instead it is employed as bait for marlin fishing.

The life history of the California flying fish is practically unknown. The eggs and larval stages have been described, but where the eggs are normally laid is a mystery. They are about one-sixteenth of an inch in diameter and rather evenly covered with filaments. Without doubt they are laid on floating objects or seaweed. Young California flying fish possess a peculiar semicircular, many-fingered outgrowth on the chin during one stage of their development. This modified barbel is red in colour.

Cods and Their Relatives —Leading Foodfish

THE CODS and their relatives are important to us as foodfish. The cod, tomcod, haddock, pollack, coalfish, cusk, ling, whiting, hake, and stockfish, all of which are used for food, are among the 150 known species of a single family (Gadidae). Mostly they inhabit northern seas; relatively few are found in the tropics or Southern Hemisphere. They spend a good deal of time on or near the bottom, but are not deep sea dwellers. The largest member is the Atlantic cod; most, however, are much smaller, weighing less than five pounds.

The grenadiers and rattails (family Macruridae) are deep-sea creatures with long, tapering bodies; both the second dorsal fin and anal fin run into the pointed tail fin with no perceptible break. This large family is found in all of the oceans, including the Arctic and Antarctic.

The fishes of this order show a peculiar mixture of both primitive and advanced characteristics. Their distinguishing features include the arrangement of bones in the skull; the position of the ventral fins in front of the pectorals, near the throat; and the lack of spines in the fins (save for a single one in the dorsal of some of the grenadiers), which gives them their scientific name, order Anacanthini ("without spines").

The Atlantic Cod, *Gadus callarias*, annually provides the fishermen on the North American banks off the north-eastern coast of that continent with more than a billion pounds of fish. Newfoundland takes almost half of this, with Canada, France, the United States, and Portugal sharing most of the rest. Other European countries, however, are also represented on the Banks.

Cod held first place in the New England fisheries for many years and was a mainstay of early American economy. One of the principal reasons for this was that cod salts down especially well, and salting was the only way large quantities of fish could be preserved in those days. With the development of modern methods of refrigeration, the haddock has supplanted the cod because it can be filleted more easily and is somewhat more available geographically.

Today codfish fillets and steaks are principally sold fresh or frozen. Some, however, are salted, smoked, or processed into fish flakes. Codfish oil, or cod-liver oil, was the first economical source of Vitamin D, the sunshine vitamin, and although it is still an important one, it is at present much more important for the Vitamin A it contains.

Most American fishermen catch cod with otter trawls (nets dragged along the bottom, with two boards to keep the mouth of the net open). Sinking gill-nets, traps, and pound-nets (large fixed nets with small openings) are also employed. Hook-and-line fishing is used extensively by Europeans, some of the long lines carrying as many as three thousand hooks.

Trawling and line fishing are employed a great deal because cod live on or near the bottom, belonging to that great group of commercially important fishes called "ground-fish", which includes the various cods and their relatives (haddock, pollack, coalfish, ling, cusk, hake, and whiting), the flatfishes (halibut, flounders, turbots, and soles), the rockfishes (rosefish, bocaccio, chillipepper, etc.) and the sablefish.

Atlantic cod are found in water as deep as 250 fathoms but in the western North Atlantic are rarely taken deeper than 150 fathoms. They prefer cold water, not inhabiting any warmer than 50 degrees F. They therefore frequent the coast of Connecticut, New York, and New Jersey only during the colder months, and farther north move offshore during the summer. In Europe the Atlantic cod straggles as far south as the Bay of Biscay. It is an important foodfish in the Irish and North Seas and in Scandinavian waters.

IT SWELLS EUROPEAN AND AMERICAN LARDERS

One of the most important foodfishes of the world, the Atlantic cod is at home in the cold waters of the North Atlantic. The flesh is not especially tasty, but has been a staple food for hundreds of years. The crude oil from the cod's liver is used in tanning leather, in making soap, and in tempering steel; refined, it is a popular source of vitamins.

Commercially caught cod generally range from two and one-half to twenty-five pounds, but fifty-pound individuals are not unusual. The largest Atlantic cod on record was more than six feet long and weighed more than 211 pounds.

Atlantic cod mature from the age of two years on, roughly half of them being capable of reproduction by the time they are five years

FASCINATING NATURAL ENTERTAINER

Although some observers maintain that flying fish flap their winglike fins and fly like birds, careful studies have proved otherwise. Swimming rapidly on the surface, into the wind, they gain sufficient momentum to enable them to thrust their bodies out of the water; at this point they spread their wings and glide, taking full advantage of the air currents. The speed and duration of the flight varies considerably among the some 60 known species. The most common Atlantic Ocean species, the two-wing flying fish, is also found in the warm portions of the Indian and Pacific Oceans. See *page 1496.*

Marine Studios, Marineland, Florida

FATHER SEAHORSE GIVES BIRTH

It is the male seahorse that carries the young around in a pouch on his abdomen and finally, with much apparent effort, launches them into the world. Here a baby is shown just emerging while another clings to the twig on the right and a third one swims above it. *See page 1517.*

old. This is an extremely prolific species; a forty-inch female can produce annually from three to four million eggs, and one seventy-five-pound specimen was estimated to contain more than nine million. The season for spawning varies greatly from region to region, beginning as early as January in some places and ending as late as October in others. The eggs are buoyant and roughly one-sixteenth of an inch in diameter. Depending upon the temperature, they hatch in ten to twenty days. Development takes as long as forty days if the salt water is as cold as 32 degrees F.

The newly hatched cod is about five thirty-seconds of an inch long and floats upside down, being held in that position by its yolk sac, which is lighter than water, for about two days. For the following two and one-half months the baby Atlantic cod remains a member of the plankton—the enormous mass of floating or weakly swimming organisms of the surface of the ocean. It feeds on various tiny animals that float there along with it, and is fed upon in turn by others. When about one inch long it sinks to the bottom. By this time it has assumed the general shape of the adult fish.

The food of the Atlantic cod is most varied, and the fish feeds both on the bottom and in mid-water, and occasionally at the surface. Squid, clams, mussels, crabs, lobsters, shrimps, sea-squirts, worms of all sorts, sea-urchins, sea-cucumbers, and brittle-stars are among the invertebrates it consumes. It also eats many kinds of fishes, including young members of its own species. Occasionally even a duck has been found in the stomach of a large cod. Rate of growth varies in different localities; off the coast of Maine, cod attain an average of fourteen pounds in two years and twenty pounds in three.

The Haddock, *Melanogrammus aeglefinus*, is the basis of the most valuable American commercial fishery of the north Atlantic Coast. About 150 million pounds are landed yearly, almost all being caught by means of otter-trawls. Most haddock is sold fresh or frozen, but a considerable amount is smoked, and then is known as finnan haddie. The haddock is also a valuable foodfish in the North Sea and around Iceland.

Haddock are similar to the Atlantic cod in having three dorsal fins, two anal fins, a single barbel under the lower jaw, and the pelvic fins located far forward in front of the pectorals, besides lacking spines in all fins. It differs from the cod in that its lateral line is black instead of light, in the presence of a dusky blotch on its sides just over the pectoral fins, and in the height and pointed triangular shape of its first dorsal fin. It does not grow nearly as large as the cod; the largest specimen ever caught was forty-four inches long and weighed between thirty-six and thirty-seven pounds.

In New England waters, haddocks mature at three or four years of age, at a weight of two to three pounds; around Newfoundland, where waters are colder, maturity is reached a year or so later. Spawning takes place from March through June. The small floating eggs hatch in two to four weeks, depending on the temperature. The young fish do not leave a planktonic existence until about three months old, when they are between one-quarter and one-half inches long. They then take up life on the sea bottom, near which they remain the rest of their lives.

Practically every kind of invertebrate inhabiting the bottom where it lives is eaten by the haddock. In addition, some swimming animals like squid, shrimps, and fish are consumed. Haddock are known to live fifteen years or longer.

The European Hake, *Merluccius merluccius*, ranges from Iceland and the coast of Norway to north-west Africa and the Mediterranean Sea. It is an important foodfish, over seventy million pounds being taken by British trawlers alone in the course of a single year.

Although the European hake feeds in midwater, it is taken by trawls (which operate along the bottom) because it rests on the bottom during the day, catching fishes, crustaceans, and squid at night. In the late spring or summer, European hake move inshore to spawn, and in the winter move off into deeper waters. The tiny eggs are planktonic, that is, they float at the surface of the sea. The young are also planktonic and do not take to the bottom until somewhat over an inch long. Female European hake grow larger and mature later than do males. A two-year-old female is about eight inches long; a thirteen-year-old fish may be more than forty inches long.

The Silver Hake, *Merluccius bilinearis*, the Pacific Hake, *Merluccius productus*, and the Stockfish, *Merluccius capensis*, are close relatives of the European hake. The silver hake, found from Newfoundland to the Bahamas, is becoming more and more popular as a foodfish; the Pacific hake, which occurs from southern California to Alaska, is hardly used for food at all. The stockfish, however, is the most important commercial fish of South Africa. It is principally taken by trawls in depths as great as one hundred fathoms, although the fish frequents water as deep as five hundred fathoms. The stockfish attains a length of four feet and feeds on midwater creatures such as squid, fish, and crustaceans.

The Burbot, *Lota lota,* is the only freshwater member of the cod family. It is found in Europe, Siberia, and northern North America as far south as Connecticut and the basins of the Great Lakes, the Missouri River, and the Columbia River. It inhabits cool streams and lakes, the latter to a depth of seven hundred feet. The burbot can easily be distinguished from all other freshwater fishes by the presence of three barbels—a single stout one on the chin and a pair of smaller ones on the snout—and by its slender, dark-coloured body with long anal and dorsal fins and the absence of spines and prominent scales.

This fish is one of North America's neglected aquatic resources. Although it is occasionally used as food, its repulsive appearance apparently discourages its wide use in the United States, despite its edibility and availability. Like its salt-water relatives, it has a liver very rich in vitamins, and this has been used as a source of these food factors by a few commercial enterprises.

The maximum size of the burbot in the United States and Canada is thirty inches with a weight of ten pounds. The species feeds voraciously, principally on other fishes and on insect larvae, crayfish, and fish eggs. In the dead of winter or very early in the spring, the burbot spawns, numerous males and females gathering together at night into balls somewhat less than three feet in diameter. Here the eggs are laid and fertilized. They are heavier than water and lie on the bottom. One female twenty-seven and one-half inches long contained well over one million of them.

Oarfishes, Opahs, and Ribbon Fishes —Including the Sea-Serpent

ALTHOUGH this group of fishes is little known—even among experts on fish—it has a claim to fame: one of its members is largely responsible for that most famous of all mythical creatures, the sea-serpent. The oarfish, which belongs to the family Regalecidae, is undoubtedly the prototype of most of the tales about snakelike sea monsters, stories which have been part and parcel of the lore of the sea since ancient times, and which regularly crop up in the newspapers and magazines of today.

The fishes of this group are most diverse in body shape. But they do have in common the ability to protrude their jaws in a way different from all other fishes (hence their scientific name, order Allotriognathi, or "strange jaws") and also a few other special features in bony structure.

The ribbon fishes or dealfishes, which have long, ribbon-shaped bodies, comprise the family Trachypteridae. The dorsal fin stretches almost the whole length of the fish and has a crest at its front end. The strange tail fin has a tiny lower lobe and a relatively tremendous, triangular, upper one. There are few species, mostly inhabiting ocean waters. The Opah, *Lampris regius*, is the sole member of the family Lampridae. It is a large fish with a body compressed from side to side but deep from back to belly and with more or less sickle-shaped pectorals, pelvics, and forward portion of the dorsal fin. The opah is of world-wide distribution in temperate and tropical seas.

The Oarfish, *Regalecus glesne*, is responsible for many of the stories about sea-serpents. Its body is long and ribbon-shaped, being extremely narrow from side to side. The fish reaches a length of twenty feet and a weight of perhaps six hundred pounds. When it swims, it throws its elongated body into great serpentine curves. Oarfish apparently live in the open ocean in many parts of the world and sometimes at least swim at the surface.

Down the whole length of the oarfish's back is the dorsal fin and the first dozen or so rays of this are greatly elongated, forming a crest or mane on top of the head. When the oarfish is excited, this crest is erected. The body is silvery and the fins coral red.

Is it any wonder that sailors, coming upon this rare, queer creature undulating its great sinuous body and flashing its brilliant red crest, have sworn that they saw a sea-serpent? Not all such tales are based on the oarfish, but undoubtedly a good many are.

Squirrel Fishes and Firefly Fishes

THE BEST-KNOWN members of this group undoubtedly are the night-prowling squirrel fishes (family Holocentridae). We know about seventy species, dwellers in tropical ocean waters, usually near shore, all around the world. These curious creatures have large eyes and rough, good-sized scales, and are usually coloured red. They rarely exceed one foot, but a few species become twice that long.

Perhaps even odder are those armoured denizens of eastern waters, the pinecone fishes (two species comprise the family Monocentridae). These small fishes have thick, spiny scales, forming a coat of mail over the body; the spines of the dorsal fin alternately angle out to the left and right, instead of being vertical as in the vast majority of fishes. Pinecone fishes are found in the tropical and temperate Indian and Pacific oceans, in fairly deep water. They possess a pair of small luminous organs located just under the lower jaw.

But light-producing organs are much more spectacularly developed in the family Anomalopidae from the tropical Pacific and Atlantic, as we shall soon see. There are two or three species, including the firefly fish. Other less well-known families are also included in this, the Order Berycoidei ("like the *Beryx*"), which takes its name from the *Beryx*, a typical genus.

This group of fishes exhibits both primitive and advanced features. The dorsal, the anal, and the ventral fins have spines in their forward portions. The ventrals are located either to the front, under the pectorals —the advanced, more "modern" arrangement—or somewhat toward the rear, but not all the way back as in the primitive, older fashion. Some of the bony structures are advanced, others primitive.

The Squirrel Fish, *Holocentrus ascensionis*, usually remains hidden during the day in its native home, and leaves its hiding place at night to forage for food. In captivity, however, it soon begins to venture forth regularly during daylight hours. A number of fishes are capable of radically changing their natural way of life when brought into captivity, adapting themselves to changed conditions in a remarkable manner, and the squirrel fish is one of them.

In common with a number of night-prowling and deep-sea fishes, the squirrel fish is coloured red. It also shows silvery and brownish tinges, and its prominent eyes are deep black. It has a single sharp spine on each cheek.

Although not caught in large numbers, this fish is often used for food when it is captured. Maximum size is usually about one foot, but two-foot specimens are known. Squirrel fish inhabit the ocean waters of Bermuda and those from Florida southward to Brazil.

The Firefly Fish, *Photoblepharon palpebratus*, swims about the coral reefs of the Banda Sea in the East Indies, flashing its light organs like a great aquatic firefly. Under each eye is a flattened, semi-circular organ, with a diameter somewhat greater than that of the eye itself, that shines with a bright light. Although this light is emitted continuously, the fish is able to turn it on or off by covering or uncovering the organs with a fold of black tissue that works very much like an eyelid. The fish reaches a length of about four inches.

The light organs are shallow and contain numerous bacteria of a special sort, which are the actual source of the light. These bacteria are evidently nurtured by special tissues or secretions of the fish, and are dependent on them for the proper kind of growth. The fish thus provides food and shelter for the bacteria, while they in turn provide their host with a continuous supply of living light.

GLOWWORM OF THE SEA

The firefly fish carries its own "searchlights"—under each eye it has a large oval spot emitting a bright light. The fish can cut off the flow of light by means of a fold of tissue that works like an eyelid. In reality the glow is produced by a colony of bacteria dwelling under the eye of the firefly fish.

No one knows to just what use the firefly fish puts its light-producing organs. Some claim that they act as searchlights, others that they are employed in signalling, but the evidence for either of these functions is inconclusive. Banda Islanders, however, make good use of them, cutting out the luminous organs and using them as bait for fishing at night. While on the hook they remain lit for as long as eight hours.

Bone-Protected Fishes—Sticklebacks and Their Relatives

IT WAS the amazing home life of the sticklebacks that first called people's attention to the complicated "love life" of certain fishes and made them aware that the world of the fish is far from a simple one. Home aquaria first became fashionable in the middle of the nineteenth century in England, and the stickleback or tittlebat was one of the most popular of aquatic pets, since it thrived and reproduced readily in captivity.

In a stormy session of the Pickwick Club, Samuel Pickwick, Esq., reported on the Theory of Tittlebats and he took no little pride in presenting his Tittlebatian Theory to the world. This was Dickens' way of poking fun at the little groups of aquatic Nature enthusiasts that sprang up in England at that time. They were the forerunners of our tropical fish and goldfish societies, of which there are several hundred in existence today.

The sticklebacks are small, fierce fishes—the largest is only about six inches long—which we find in the fresh and salt waters of the cooler parts of the Northern Hemisphere. Some species live in fresh water exclusively, others in salt. Still others, such as the threespine and fourspine sticklebacks, are found in both types and in brackish waters of varying salt content. In all species of sticklebacks, the males are good fathers—they build a nest to receive the eggs, which they guard and otherwise care for. There are about a dozen different species of sticklebacks, all members of the family Gasterosteidae.

The tube-snouts are cousins of the sticklebacks but belong to the family Aulorhynchidae. They look like very long sticklebacks. One species, *Aulorhynchus flavidus*, dwells along the Pacific coast of North

America, from southern California to Alaska. It attains a length of six and one-half inches.

The sticklebacks and their less-known relatives have a number of peculiarities in their bony structure, as well as two or more free spines in front of the dorsal fin. The pelvic fins are placed close behind the pectorals, and the body is usually either armoured along the sides with bony plates or completely encased in a series of bony rings. It was for this reason that the order was named Thoracostei, or "bony chests".

The Threespine Stickleback, *Gasterosteus aculeatus*, darts about and hovers in water the way a humming-bird does in air. Everything about this small fish seems to indicate intensity of effort, and even when it remains stationary with its tiny pectoral fins vibrating and its tail characteristically curved to one side, it appears, like a steel spring, ready to jump into action—which it does, dashing off to catch some small creature for food, to court some likely female, or to fight with some male, or other intruding fish.

Adult threespine sticklebacks are usually about two and one-quarter inches long, but in some places they grow to a length of four inches. Their spindle-shaped body seems well protected by two large spines (and one small one) on the back, one large spine on either side of the belly, and a number of flat, bony shields, or scutes, on the sides in place of ordinary scales. The mouth has numerous sharp teeth.

Good use is made of these various weapons, for sticklebacks are pugnacious, attacking fish much larger than themselves with both teeth and ventral spines. It has been claimed that the spines also afford them protection against larger fish which would otherwise eat them. Although this may be true in some instances, goodly numbers of sticklebacks are consumed by fish and birds. The number of scutes present varies from none to thirty-six, and depends on the salt content and temperature of the water in which the fish lives; the more salty the water and the lower the temperature, the greater the number of scutes.

As we have seen, threespine sticklebacks inhabit both salt and fresh waters. The species is found throughout the northern portion of the Northern Hemisphere. In North America it occurs as far south as Virginia and southern California on the coasts, and the Lake Ontario Basin inland. In a few places sticklebacks are so abundant that they are caught in great numbers; they are pressed for their oil, and the residue is used as fertilizer.

For its size the threespine stickleback is as ferocious as any fish; it kills and sometimes eats fish as large or larger than itself. It feeds principally upon small crustaceans and insects, but also eats the eggs and fry of other fishes. Its appetite is enormous. One specimen ate seventy-five quarter-inch fish within five hours, and two days later consumed sixty-two more.

The reproductive habits of the threespine stickleback are quite complicated and have been studied by numerous naturalists and experimental zoologists. During spring and summer the male develops a bright red throat and belly and selects a bit of bottom in quiet water that he defends against all other fishes, especially other male sticklebacks. He builds a nest of bits of aquatic plants, cemented together by a sticky thread-like secretion manufactured by his kidneys. Sometimes, instead of building a nest, he digs a hole in the ground and lines it with this secretion. Females are vigorously courted with zig-zag "dancing", chasing, nipping, and butting. Finally the female follows the male to his nest and enters it, or is forced to enter it—both coaxing and coercion seem to play a part in the process. She lays her relatively large eggs, measuring about one-sixteenth of an inch in diameter, and then, strangely enough, leaves by burrowing or boring a new exit from the nest, rather than backing out of the one she entered. In fact the male, sometimes at least, prevents her from backing out by nips and butts. The male then enters and fertilizes the eggs. Several females are usually enticed or driven to lay in a single nest, each being chased away when her duties have been performed. For about six days the male parent guards his nest and circulates water through it by fanning with his pectoral fins. After the young have hatched, the nest is generally torn open, but the fry are carefully returned to the site when they stray away. Finally, either the young become too adventurous for the male to control their wanderings or he loses interest in them, and the family group disperses.

The Fourspine Stickleback, *Apeltes quadracus*, differs from the three-spine species in lacking bony scutes and in the triangular cross section of its body, as well as in the number of spines in front of the dorsal fin. Common in salt and brackish water along the east coast of North America from New Brunswick and Nova Scotia to Virginia, this species is occasionally also found in fresh water. It reaches a length of about two and one-half inches, but most adults are less than one and one-half inches long.

Spawning occurs in late spring and summer. The male constructs a nest, usually near the base of some aquatic plant. With the aid of a sticky, threadlike secretion from the kidneys, he weaves the stalks together with bits of other plants, until a small, cup-shaped basket is formed. Females are then courted assiduously, and after one or more have laid their eggs in the nest, he builds a "roof" over it. This contains two tiny holes just large enough for the male to put his snout into— in order to suck fresh water over the eggs.

One male may construct a nest of three or four storeys, successively adding to the structure from the top. At the same time he must guard

BUILDING HIS NEST

The fourspine stickleback builds a nest much as a bird does. As shown in the illustration, the male weaves portions of water plants into a sort of basket, using growing stalks as the framework. After the female of his choice has laid her eggs in the nest, he roofs it over, and looks around for another mate.

them all and keep them in repair, ventilate the eggs within the lower stories, entice females to fill up the latest addition, and now and then take time off to feed. Such males with as many as four nests going at once have been described as the busiest things among fishes.

The eggs are yellowish spheres, about one-sixteenth of an inch in diameter. They hatch in about six days at 72 degrees Fahrenheit.

Seahorses and Their Relatives

To MANY people the little seahorse is one of the most fascinating of fishes. Its small head actually resembles a horse's, and the creature holds it upright as its swims along with an air of serious dignity. No other fish is so frequently used as a motif for jewellery, book-ends, ash-trays, lamps and other decorative furniture, to say nothing of all the bookplates, advertisements, trade marks and emblems in which seahorses have appeared. The seahorse has become the symbol of ocean life.

But the seahorse is only one of the odd types we find in this order. Trumpet fishes, cornet fishes, snipefishes, and shrimpfishes are also among the important members of the group. Its variety is one of its most impressive features. Looking casually at the three suborders (each contains two families), we are hard put to discover much resemblance among them. One thing they all seem to have in common, however—a small mouth located at the end of a tubelike snout. It is inside their bodies, rather than outside, that these fishes are most alike, and the order name, Hemibranchi ("half-gills") highlights the fact that their gills are small and differently shaped from those of other fishes.

Joined, bony armour completely covers the seahorses and pipefishes (family Syngnathidae). We know more than 150 different pipefishes, ranging from tubelike forms with well-developed caudal fins to others with a grasping tail and a head and body that remind us of the typical seahorse. Pipefishes, as a general rule, are at home in weedy shallows along tropical shores, but we do encounter a few in temperate ocean waters. Several species frequently enter streams, and there are some tropical ones found only in fresh water. The largest forms are about two feet long.

One of the rarest and most amazing of seahorselike fishes is the Leafy Seadragon, *Phycodurus eques*, of South Australia. Its head, body and tail are covered with leaf-like growths—the whole animal looks for all the world like a piece of seaweed and is a miracle of natural camouflage. It is about one foot long.

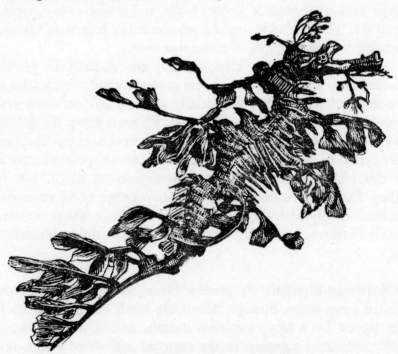

AN ANIMATED PIECE OF SEAWEED

One of the oddities of the fish world is the leafy seadragon, a dweller in Australian waters. This relative of the seahorse has extensive leaflike growths of skin which stream out around it in the water, so that the fish can rarely be distinguished from the seaweed among which it lives. Only three or four specimens of the leafy seadragon have ever been found; these strange creatures measured some twelve inches in length.

Curiously enough, in all of the pipefishes and seahorses the female, after producing the eggs, turns them over to the male for care. He carries them either in a broodpouch or attached to the under-part of his body. Nature, we see, has devised many ways of accomplishing a single end. (In the related family Solenostomidae of the Indian and west Pacific oceans, however, the female carries the eggs.)

The trumpet fishes (family Aulostomidae) and the cornet fishes (family Fistulariidae) are each of a small group of tropical ocean fishes. Superficially, the trumpet fishes appear to combine the features of the pipefishes and seahorses and the barracudas, while the cornet fishes at first glance look like marine gars (needle fishes). There are about half a dozen kinds of cornet fishes; they attain lengths of six feet or more, and are useful for food. The trumpet fishes—we know only one or two species —grow to be about twenty inches long.

The snipefishes (family Macrorhamphosidae) possess an unmistakable shape with a long snout, a short body, and a single strong spine in the dorsal fin. They inhabit tropical seas, and the largest of the dozen or so species reaches a length of about one foot.

The shrimpfishes (family Centriscidae) are encased in plates of translucent bone. Their two dorsal fins project straight out to the rear, being located where the tail fin usually is. The tail fin is turned so that it projects downward next to the anal. There is sharp disagreement as to how the shrimpfishes swim. Some observers claim they swim vertically, that is, belly first with the long snout pointed upwards. Others claim they swim with the snout pointed down, the back proceeding first. Still others state that they progress in an ordinary fashion, horizontally with the snout first. There are less than six species of these small fishes, inhabiting the tropical Indian and western Pacific Oceans.

The Northern Pipefish, *Syngnathus fuscus*, has a long body, covered with ribbed bony plates through which the small fins project. Its long snout is tipped by a tiny, toothless mouth, and it feeds principally on small crustaceans common in the seaweed and shore plants among which it lives. This species is found from Nova Scotia to North Carolina, usually quite close to shore. It reaches a length of one foot.

During courtship the male and female embrace, their bodies making two intertwining S-shaped curves. The female deposits a batch of eggs by means of a long ovipositor (egg-laying organ) into a pouch that the male has on his under-side. The pair then separates, and the male works the spawn farther down into the pouch with various gyrations before egg deposition is commenced again. The eggs remain in the pouch for some time, being carried about by the male until they hatch.

Because of this peculiar reversal of the usual part played by the sexes in reproduction, male pipefishes were for many years quite understandably thought to be the females. After their correct sex was first reported, in 1831, a forty-year controversy ensued before the matter was finally settled. In some species of pipefishes the eggs are carried in open grooves along the belly rather than in closed pouches.

The Western Atlantic Seahorse, *Hippocampus hudsonius*, has a head like that of a horse, an external skeleton like that of an insect, a prehensile, or grasping, tail like that of a monkey, eyes that can be moved independently like those of a chameleon, and a pouch for carrying its offspring like that of a kangaroo. Few animals have such an extraordinary assortment of characteristics!

Seahorses are found in tropical and temperate seas throughout the world. They usually inhabit shallow water, but some have been found in floating seaweed far from land. About fifty different species are known. The largest, *Hippocampus ingens*, of the west coast of the Americas from the extreme southern part of California to northern Peru, attains a length of one foot. The common western Atlantic seahorse averages about four inches in length and has been known to reach seven and one-half. The Dwarf Seahorse, *Hippocampus zosterae*, of Florida never exceeds two inches.

The unique shape of seahorses, with their head held at a right angle to their upright body, makes them resemble nothing so much as a knight on the chessboard. The whole body is encased in jointed armour —an external skeleton that they possess in addition to the more usual internal skeleton of all backboned animals. The mouth is a small, traplike affair located at the tip of the long snout. More than half of the total length of the seahorse is made up of the tail, which is rectangular in cross-section, flexible and prehensile. The fish spends much time holding fast to undersea objects by means of this organ.

The deliberate behaviour of the seahorse gives it a dignity lacking in most fishes. Its progress is always slow, for the fish must depend upon the movements of its small dorsal and pectoral fins to swim about. Since these fins are more or less transparent and unnoticeable, the seahorse gives the appearance of moving through water without effort of any sort. Actually each part of these fins may vibrate back and forth as fast as thirty-five times per second. The usual position of the body is more or less vertical; horizontal or head-down positions are taken only infrequently.

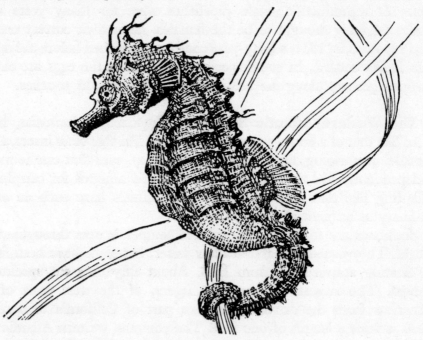

HORSE OF THE SEA

An object of great interest to visitors at an aquarium is the seahorse. This curious fish swims along with what impresses us as remarkable dignity, or else it rests on some underwater object, to which it attaches itself by its tail. It is the father seahorse, pictured above, that cares for the young—he possesses a pouch, in which he carries the eggs about until they are hatched.

Seahorses feed on small crustaceans which they snap up with their tiny, toothless jaws and swallow whole. They pursue this small prey with gravity and preciseness at the same slow pace that seems to mark their whole existence. Because of their finicky feeding habits—and also their absolute dependence on pure sea water—seahorses are difficult to maintain in captivity. This is too bad, because otherwise no other aquatic creature would approach their popularity as pets.

Reproduction in the western Atlantic seahorse takes place during the late spring and summer. The female seahorse, not the male, is said to do the courting. At any rate, she grows an ovipositor, a special organ with which she deposits her eggs in the pouch of the male. This pouch is located on his belly just before the tail and has a single small

[12-13]

The western Atlantic seahorse has the head of a horse, the external skeleton of an insect, the prehensile tail of a New World monkey, the independently roving eyes of a chameleon, and the pouch of a kangaroo for carrying its offspring. In spite of this extraordinary assortment of characteristics, the intriguing little animal is a fish. The female does the courting, and lays her eggs in the pouch of the male. They are fertilized there, the pouch seals over, and the male is left in the odd position of being a "mother" in the placental mammal sense of the word—oxygen and food are supplied to the young, and waste products are removed. When the offspring are ready to take their place in the world, the pouch opens and their father, with the dignity characteristic of seahorses, "gives birth". See page 1517

[12-14]

The vast order of spiny-rayed fish is the largest single group of bony fishes and includes among its 75 families the bass, sunfish and perch. The rock bass, a rather common gamefish of the cool, clear waters of the north-eastern part of North America ranges south through the Mississippi basin. Averaging eight to ten inches in length and about a pound in weight, rock bass are difficult to spot as they change colour rapidly, blending with their surroundings.   *See page 1533*

[12-14A]

The warmouth has a relatively large mouth like that of the rock bass and is about the same size. It inhabits the warmer lakes, ponds and larger streams of the Mississippi basin and Gulf states. All the members of this family feed on insects and small fish, and the males of many species construct nests and care for the eggs and young.
See page 1533

opening at its front end. The eggs are fertilized at this time. While they are contained within the pouch, the opening is sealed, so it is obvious that the male must at least supply oxygen to his growing off-spring. The highly developed state of the walls of the pouch during incubation indicates that food, too, is supplied to the young. Of course, their waste products must also be removed. The father seahorse, then, truly acts like a mother, carrying and nurturing the young until birth.

In the western Atlantic seahorse, the young are born after about forty-five days of incubation within the male's pouch. If the struggles and gyrations of the father fish are any indication, getting rid of his brood is a difficult and exhausting task. Frequently the male presses his full pouch against rocks or shells as if trying to dislodge the young. The 150 to 200 babies, each a quarter of an inch long, may be born over a period of several days. The dwarf seahorse has much smaller broods, numbering less than ten young, and the whole procedure of birth may take place in less than a quarter of an hour.

Silversides, Mullets, and Barracudas

IN THIS group we find creatures that are fish food, fish eaters, man food—and man-eaters. Some are so small you can catch them with your hands; others are longer than a man, and catching them requires great skill and strength.

A silvery band along each side helps us to recognize most of the more than 150 species of silversides. (They make up the family Ather-inidae.) Besides the silversides proper, this family has other members —the whitebaits, the Australian rainbow fishes, the grunion and the jack-smelt. Although they are mostly at home in tropical oceans, many of them regularly enter brackish water, and a number spend their whole lives in the fresh waters of streams or lakes. The largest species—dwellers in the temperate zones—reach a length of between one and two feet.

The mullets are no small family, either. We know more than one hundred different kinds (family Mugilidae). The largest species reach a good two and one-half feet and a weight of nine pounds. Several are valuable as food; for example, *Mugil dobula* is one of the two most important commercial fishes of Australia. During the spawning season many of the mullets leave the tropical or temperate ocean waters, in which they spend most of their time, for brackish or fresh waters. A number are permanent freshwater inhabitants.

Swift hunters and ferocious killers, the barracudas—there are twenty different kinds or so in the family Sphyraenidae—prowl all the warm seas. One of the largest of these pikelike fishes is the great barracuda of the western Atlantic, a creature as fearsome as any we encounter on land. Not so formidable are the other members of this order, the threadfins (family Polynemidae). These fishes live near the shores of tropical seas, sometimes entering fresh water, perhaps to spawn. Adults are usually less than one foot long, but a few species exceed six feet. They have peculiar pectoral fins, each one of which is separated into two parts; the upper part is quite ordinary, but the lower part consists of about a half-dozen long, separate threadlike rays, after which the fish are named. In the Indo-Pacific regions, the threadfins (there are about twenty-five different kinds) are sought as food.

All the fishes in this order—Percesoces, meaning "perch-pikes"—have spines on their fins. Still, unlike the true spiny-rayed fishes, which we shall encounter in the next chapter, their ventral fins are located back on the belly rather than near the throat. They have two dorsal fins.

The Common Silverside, *Menidia menidia,* dwells in enormous numbers along the shores of the Atlantic from Nova Scotia to Florida. Great schools of these small, light-coloured fish can often be seen in very shallow water in bays or inlets or near sandy or gravelly beaches. They frequently venture into brackish water.

Silversides are characterized by their slender shape, two dorsal fins and a wide silvery band that runs from head to tail. They reach a maximum length of six inches. Their food consists of all sorts of tiny creatures, belonging to the crustacean, mollusc, and worm groups of invertebrates. They also eat algae and other very small plants, and fish eggs, too—including their own.

The common silverside spawns from early spring to late summer, depending on the latitude. The eggs are about one-sixteenth of an inch in diameter and are provided with a tuft of long, gelatinous threads. Ripe fish gather in shallow water to deposit their eggs which, being slightly heavier than sea water, sink to the bottom, and become attached to plants and other underwater objects by means of the sticky threads. Hatching takes place in one or two weeks or more, depending on the temperature.

This species is not ordinarily used for food, although its close relative *Menidia beryllina* provides the delicacy, whitebait. The common silverside is nevertheless of no little economic importance, because of the abundant food it provides for so many other larger food and gamefish.

The Grunion, *Leuresthes tenuis*, is regularly caught with the bare hands—on land! This unbelievable mode of fishing is made possible by the equally unbelievable spawning habits of the fish, which lays its eggs out of water on various beaches of southern and Baja California.

From March until July or August, grunion spawn a day or two after each new and full moon. They begin their reproductive activities from fifteen to forty minutes after the night high tide. At this time grunion can be seen riding in with the waves and swimming farther on to the beach as the waves recede, thus being left stranded on the sand. Each incoming female is accompanied by several males. After she "hits the beach", she digs herself, tail first, into the soft wet sand by twisting and turning, until she is buried up to her pectoral fins. The males curve around her on top of the sand as closely as possible. The female then lays a batch of eggs underground. As she struggles to free herself, leaving her eggs behind, the milt (sexual secretion) of the males is carried down to fertilize them.

Now both sexes wiggle back toward the sea, catching up with a wave that eventually carries them back into the deeper water. The whole process may take less than half a minute, but several minutes out of water seem to do the grunion no harm.

The eggs remain in the moist sand until the next series of extra-high

tides, two weeks later, come and wash them out. Two or three minutes
after the eggs have been freed, the baby grunions hatch out and are
carried out to sea. The marvellous adjustment of the fish to its living
conditions is apparent. The eggs are laid just after the extra-high
tides following the new and full moons, tides that will not be equalled
in height for two weeks. Thus for this length of time the eggs will be
safe from premature exposure. Nor will the eggs hatch if the succeeding
extra-high tide should fail to uncover them. They will remain, development suspended, until the next one, that is, until a month after they
were laid. So long as they remain covered with sand the eggs will
not hatch. In fact, the eggs are ready to hatch about a week after being
laid. They have even successfully developed in running water in the
laboratory, showing that burying in sand is not necessary. The eggs
are about one-sixteenth of an inch in diameter and salmon pink

FISHES THAT COME ASHORE TO LAY THEIR EGGS

Sometimes thousands of grunion are seen at one time on the beaches of California, for
these fish lay their eggs on land. There the eggs remain until a very high tide carries them
back to the ocean, where they hatch. Shown in the foreground is the female depositing
the eggs, with the male circling about her. Their sojourn ashore rarely lasts more than
a few minutes, but they can remain out of water for quite a while without harm.

in colour. The newly hatched young are about one-quarter of an inch long and relatively well developed; they are able to swim immediately.

During the height of a spawning run there may be so many grunion on the beach that walking there without stepping on them is impossible. The sight of thousands of these slender, silvery, six-inch fish on a moonlit beach is a memorable one. In order to protect the grunion—an excellent foodfish which was becoming quite scarce—all types of special grunion-collecting equipment, such as nets, have been forbidden, and only the bare hands may be used to capture them. In addition, the state of California has ruled that no grunion at all may be taken during April and May.

Most of the grunion's life is apparently spent near sandy beaches from Point Conception south to the northern portion of Baja California. This is the only place in the world where these fish exist. Young grunion grow rapidly, and by the spring following their hatching they are about five inches long and soon are ready to spawn themselves. They usually live to be two or three years old, and rarely four.

The Striped Mullet, *Mugil cephalus*, feeds on tiny floating plants which it sifts out of the water, on algae which it scrapes off stones, pilings, and the leaves of aquatic plants, and on organic matter from the bottom, which it sifts out of mouthfuls of silt and mud. To help it digest its food, which is mostly vegetable matter, the striped mullet has a gizzard, very similar to that found in birds, where the food is ground up by the action of thick muscular walls covered inside with a horny lining. The mullet's intestine is also relatively long and coiled, permitting more complete digestion and absorption.

When it is young, the striped mullet has the more usual type of short intestine and a good set of teeth. It feeds on small floating animals and plants at this time. As it grows older, its teeth become reduced to tiny bristles, while its intestine becomes longer and more coiled. These changes occur at the beginning of adult feeding habits. Experts disagree as to just where young striped mullet are born, that is, whether the adults lay their eggs in bays and other inside waters, or along exposed shores. We have little scientific information about the eggs, even though spawning fish have once been described. According to this report, each ripe female was accompanied by several smaller males who huddled close to her on all sides during the process of egg laying. It is agreed that reproduction takes place from November to February in Florida waters.

The striped mullet has a world-wide distribution in temperate and warm seas. Along the Atlantic coast of North America it is found from Maine to Florida but rarely occurs north of Cape Cod. Its range extends along the Gulf coast, Mexico, Central America, and south past Brazil. On the Pacific coast it is found from central California to Chile. It is present in the Mediterranean and was well known to the ancients there. It ranges down the west coast of Africa at least as far as the Congo, and all around the Indian Ocean. It is rare in the Indo-Australian archipelago, but is a common fish along much of the Asiatic coast, including the Philippines and Japan.

In many places in the Orient and in Hawaii, the striped mullet is reared in brackish or sea-water ponds. In nature the fish often ventures into the brackish or fresh waters of streams.

Wherever it occurs in large schools, the striped mullet is an important foodfish. In the southern United States about thirty-seven million pounds are taken each year. On the west coast the fish is beginning to become popular as a foodfish, and as a gamefish, too, when taken on light tackle with a dry fly. It grows to a length of about two feet.

The Great Barracuda, *Sphyraena barracuda*, deserves its reputation for ferocity. It has been called the "tiger of the sea"; few fishes seem better equipped, both mentally and physically, to destroy other living creatures. Fearless and apparently inquisitive, a barracuda is not frightened away by the antics of a swimming man as would be almost any other fish. Many of the supposed shark attacks on bathers in the West Indies are the work of this dreadful fish.

With one swipe of its great jaws a barracuda can remove the whole lower-leg muscle of a man or maim his arm or leg so badly as to make surgical amputation necessary. The fish's teeth are pointed, razor-sharp, and they overlap one another, fitting rather closely between the corresponding members on the opposite jaw. From two to four large canines (fangs)—extending three-quarters of an inch beyond the gums in fair-sized specimens—are located on either side of the front part of the upper jaw. One or two are placed at the tip of the lower jaw. Whenever teeth become broken or worn out, they are replaced by new ones that grow in beside the old.

The long pikelike body of the great barracuda seems admirably adapted to sudden dashes through the water. The fish's usual food consists of other fish, which it carefully stalks, then attacks with terrific speed, the strike being almost too fast for the eye to see. Great barracuda have been seen herding a group of snappers, grunts, angel-fishes, and others, and not one of this group of prospective prey was able to make a dash to liberty.

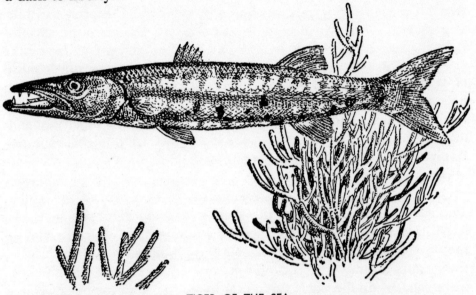

TIGER OF THE SEA

The great barracuda, at home in the waters off the West Indies, Bermuda, and Florida, will attack almost any living thing, including human beings. The sharp, pointed teeth of this tiger of the sea can with one bite practically amputate a man's arm or leg. Barracudas often grow to a length of six feet or more.

The reproductive habits of the great barracuda are a mystery, although it is suspected that it spawns in the early spring and that its eggs float on the surface of the ocean. It grows to be ten feet long, but few individuals exceed half that length.

Rarely is a great barracuda ever found farther north than the Carolinas. Small specimens, however, are not uncommon in Bermuda. Its usual home is the West Indies, but it also occurs south to Brazil. This seems to be the most dangerous to man of all the barracudas. The Northern Barracuda, *Sphyraena borealis*, of the east coast of the United States and the Pacific Barracuda, *Sphyraena argentea*, of the west coast are both completely harmless. At least one species in the East Indies, however, has been authentically credited with attacks on men.

The Spiny-Rayed Fishes

IF FISHES interest you at all, you will discover a whole world of wonder in this, the largest single group of bony fishes. Among its species, perch, bass, and sunfish are the delight of both sport and food fishermen; and the pompano and snappers are eagerly sought table delicacies. Bluefish are so ferocious that they might be called "wolves of the sea", and the dorado, or dolphin, is a shining example of incarnate, streamlined speed.

Queer habits and abilities are common in members of this order. The conchfish dwells within the shell of a living giant sea snail; the leaf-fish is a master of camouflage in imitating dead leaves floating in the water; and the archer fish shoots tiny "bullets" of water. Finally, the grunts, drums, croakers, pigfish, and weak fish have the ability to make sounds—in the water and out of it—to such an extent that schools of certain species around a vessel at anchor will keep the people aboard awake all night.

In a number of ways we can consider the spiny-rayed fishes the peak development of present-day forms—that is, the highest point of a whole line of evolutionary progress. Judged by the number of species alive today, they are the most successful of all of the orders of fishes. In total number of individuals, they stand far ahead of all other salt-water fishes. The spiny-rayed fishes are, in effect, the typical modern fish.

Being typical, they lack the radical, bizarre anatomical features possessed by more highly specialized—and therefore more limited—fishes. They are, nevertheless, extremely different from family to family. These two facts make it difficult, if not impossible, to define them accurately, except in technical terms meaningful only to the expert. Moreover, the experts themselves have had difficulty in defining the group and in deciding exactly what fishes should or should not be included in it.

This vast order, the Percoidei ("perchlike") contains about seventy-five families, including such well-known fishes as the perches, sunfishes, basses, groupers, snooks, snappers, grunts, porgies, weakfishes, goatfishes, and jacks. They have spines in some of their fins, and the pelvic fins, if present, are located well forward, near or directly under the pectorals. Although they have many characteristics in common, they are perhaps best identified by those features they do not possess. For example, they lack the Weberian apparatus of the minnows and catfishes, the irregular shapes of the flatfishes, the accessory gill chambers of the climbing perch, and the peculiar arrangement of cheekbones of the scorpion fishes. Only a fraction of the large number of existing families is mentioned here, since many of them are unknown except to scientists and local specialists.

The Yellow Perch, *Perca flavescens*, furnishes both commercial and sports fishermen with a highly valued catch. About six million pounds are taken commercially each year in the Great Lakes region, and no one knows the weight of the millions of yellow perch caught by anglers. We find the fish east of the Rockies from northern Canada south to Kansas, Missouri, Illinois, Indiana, Ohio, Pennsylvania, and South Carolina.

Yellow perch inhabit lakes, ponds, and the quiet parts of streams. They have been introduced into the West Coast and farther south, but these transplantations have not been very successful. Yellowish sides with six to eight dark vertical bars distinguish the yellow perch from other North American freshwater fishes. The largest specimen ever taken by rod-and-reel weighed four pounds, three and one-half ounces, but the usual maximum weight is about one pound with a length of about twelve to fifteen inches.

In the spring, long, adhesive bands, containing tens of thousands of eggs, are laid over weeds, sticks, and sunken branches, usually at night. The eggs hatch in somewhat less than a month. The food of the yellow perch is quite varied, including insect larvae and adults, crustaceans, molluscs, worms, fishes, and algae and other plant material. When adult, the fish no longer eats plants, but only animal matter.

The perches, pikeperches, and darters comprise the family Percidae, a freshwater group with about ten species in northern Asia and all of Europe except Spain and Portugal, and with a few more than 100 species in North America, east of the Rockies. The vast majority of the different species are darters, which are exclusively North American. The largest members of this family range up to about three feet in length and twenty-five pounds in weight.

The Pikeperch, *Stizostedion vitreum*, has a tricky name. It is indeed related to the perch, but not to the pike. In appearance it is not at all pikelike, being approximately spindle-shaped and having two dorsal fins and relatively short jaws. It is at home east of the Rockies from central and southern Canada to Nebraska, Arkansas, Alabama, Georgia, and North Carolina. Not native to New Jersey, Connecticut, and eastern Pennsylvania, it has been successfully introduced there, as well as into many bodies of water within its original range. It prefers large, cool lakes and clear rivers.

Pikeperch are flesh-eaters, feeding mostly on other fishes, but also on insects, crustaceans, and amphibians. Although specimens weighing as much as twenty-five pounds have been reported, any more than ten are rare, and the usual weights run to less than five. The record angler's catch was slightly more than three feet long and weighed twenty-two and one-quarter pounds.

Shortly after the ice melts or in the very early spring, pikeperch spawn. They often migrate up small streams to lay their numerous eggs, but sometimes deposit them in the shallow parts of lakes. Spawning occurs at night. The eggs are heavier than water, and lie on the bottom. They are about one-twelfth of an inch in diameter. Hatching takes place in a week to a month, depending on the temperature.

There are three different pikeperches generally recognized in North America, and altogether they yield in the neighbourhood of ten million pounds of highly edible fish to commercial fishermen in the United States—almost entirely in the region of the Great Lakes. In addition, a considerably larger amount is imported from Canada. Two of the generally recognized pikeperches, the Yellow Pikeperch, or Walleye Pike, and the Blue Pikeperch, are geographical varieties of *Stizostedion vitreum*. The third is a separate, somewhat smaller species, the Sauger, *Stizostedion canadense*, which occasionally cross-breeds with the yellow pikeperch.

The Johnny Darter, *Boleosoma nigrum*, lives on the bottom of lakes and streams, mostly in shallow water among rocks, or on gravel and sand. It is a small fish, becoming as a rule not more than two and one-half inches long at the maximum, although specimens nearly an inch longer have been measured. Its food consists of small crustaceans and insects and algae. Sometimes Johnny darters eat the eggs of other fishes. This species is widely distributed from southern Canada to Colorado, Alabama, and North Carolina.

Johnny darters spawn in the late spring and summer. The eggs are laid on the under-surface of a submerged stone, mussel shell, or other object; the pair swims upside down during the process of egg laying. The male, who is somewhat larger than the female and more strikingly coloured than she is during the reproductive season, guards the eggs. He also circulates water around them by vibrating his tail under them, and cleans them by turning on his back and brushing them with his body and pectoral fins. The eggs are amber in colour and about one-sixteenth of an inch in diameter. They hatch in about three weeks at about 65 degrees Fahrenheit.

There are about one hundred different darters, all of them in North America, but none in the Pacific drainage. They are small fishes; one species is adult at the size of one inch, and the "giant" of the group is the Logperch, *Percina caprodes*, which attains a length of eight inches. Most darters live in streams, always on or near the bottom and frequently among the stones in riffles. Species that do not exhibit parental care of their eggs, lay them on plants or on the bottom, or bury them in sand, and then abandon them.

The Thin Snook, *Centropomis undecimalis*, you can most easily recognize by its low, sloping forehead, its pointed snout, and its under-shot jaw. This fish is used both for food and sport. It occurs from Florida and the Gulf Coast south to Brazil, frequently travelling up rivers for many miles. The thin snook feeds on a variety of creatures such as smaller fishes, crabs, and shrimps. It attains weights of more than fifty pounds but averages only about four. Very little is known about the life history of this fish, although it is an important foodfish along the Gulf Coast.

The snooks belong to the family Centropomidae. They occur along the coasts on both sides of South and Central America as far north as Florida in the east and Baja California in the west. They are also found along the shores of tropical west Africa. There are at least eight different species. Other fishes included in the family are the numerous, small glassfishes of shallow, salt, brackish, and fresh waters of the Indian and western Pacific regions, and the perchlike fishes of the genus *Lates*, which are important foodfishes in Africa and southeastern Asia and the East Indies.

The Conchfish, *Astrapogon stellatus*, often makes its home in the cavity of very large marine snails called conchs. These molluscs, belonging to the genus *Strombus*, are used as food, and when they are taken off the bottom they close up the opening to their shells, trapping inside any small conchfish that is using them as a shelter. Later, while lying on the bottom of the collecting boat or in the market, the snail relaxes and the fish falls out, much to the surprise of any beholder.

Not all conchs contain conchfish, however, nor does every conchfish live within a conch. These fish also inhabit living sponges and bivalves and the empty shells of dead conchs; they most probably make use of a wide variety of objects for shelter. When kept in an aquarium, they hide during the day, appearing only when it is dark; most likely in nature they rarely leave their conch except at night.

The colour of the conchfish is quite variable. At night it may be almost white, and by day, dark brown. Sometimes a single, slanted, very dark line runs across the cheek; at other times there may be four different lines on the head and body. The pelvic fins are unusually long, but whether they serve any special purpose is unknown. A length of two inches is attained.

Conchfish feed largely on small crustaceans. They occur in Bermuda, the West Indies, and southern Florida. Reproduction begins in August. As in many other species of cardinal fishes, the male carries the eggs around in his mouth.

The cardinal fishes make up the family Apogonidae. They are small fishes, found generally in shallow, tropical salt waters, and comprise one of the most populous groups living among East Indian coral reefs and around the Philippines. Several inhabit depths as great as sixteen hundred feet, and some live in fresh water. Many of them are red or pink in colour.

The Smallmouth Black Bass, *Micropterus dolomieu*, rivals the best of the trouts and salmons in popularity as a freshwater gamefish. Originally distributed through most of the Great Lakes drainage and the Ohio, Tennessee, and upper Mississippi river systems, the smallmouth black bass has been introduced into practically every state and most of the Canadian provinces. It has also been quite successfully transplanted to South Africa and less so to the British Isles and the European continent. Its favourite living places are clear, cool lakes and streams that are not too small and have little vegetation or mud.

The average adult smallmouth black bass weighs from one and one-half to three pounds, but especially large ones may attain weights of more than eleven pounds. Such specimens are usually quite old. Experts have found that the smallmouth can live to be at least fourteen years old in nature. It grows rather rapidly when an ample food supply is present, and may reach a length of ten inches in three to six years; it becomes sexually mature in four to six years.

The spawning season begins when the water becomes sufficiently warmed by the spring sun, that is, from late April to the end of June, depending on the latitude and weather. The males gather over sunny, gravel- or rock-covered areas, usually where the water is three to six feet deep. Each male establishes a territory that he vigorously defends against other fish, especially other bass.

By assuming a nearly vertical position, head uppermost, and fanning the bottom with his tail, the male starts to construct his nest. He roots up the bottom, loosening debris so that it may be fanned away, and carries larger pebbles and other objects away in his mouth.

The nest may take two days or more to build. It is a saucer-shaped depression, as much as four feet in diameter, if the male that made it is a large one. No speck of sediment is allowed to settle for long on any stone within the nest, nor is any fish, crayfish, snail, or worm allowed to remain in it. The male cleans and guards his nest continuously.

Soon females approach the nesting area, and the males try to drive them into their nests. Eventually a female enters one of the nests and lays her adhesive eggs on a small patch of the polished stones lying on the bottom. More than one female may spawn in the nest of a single male. The females retire after laying their eggs, their duties as a parent being completed.

It is the male's job to care for the eggs and young. He gently fans the eggs with his pectoral and tail fins and attacks all creatures that come near them. When they hatch, three or four days later, he also fans and watches over the helpless fry. In three to twelve days, the young begin to swim about. Then the male conducts them into shallow water near shore where he continues to stand guard over them, usually for two to nine more days, but sometimes for as long as twenty-eight.

The food of recently hatched smallmouth black bass consists of small crustaceans like water fleas. As they grow larger, the fish begin to eat insects. When about one and one-half inches long, they start to catch small fishes, and at twice this size crayfish are added to their diet.

The Largemouth Black Bass, *Micropterus salmoides*, as you might expect, may be distinguished from the smallmouth by the size of its mouth, which extends back past the eye. Also, it has an almost complete division between the two parts of its dorsal fin. Scientists at present recognize three species of black basses besides the smallmouth and largemouth. The habits of all of these are basically alike, but they differ in a number of details. For example, the largemouth black bass is typically found in weedy, mud-bottomed, still, or sluggishly moving fresh waters, in contrast to the smallmouth which occurs in cooler, clearer, generally more rapid waters.

The largemouth originally lived farther south than the smallmouth: its range extended from northern Canada through the Great Lakes and Mississippi river systems to Florida and north-eastern Mexico. Because of its greater adaptability to warm, still waters, the large-mouth black bass has been employed extensively in pond culture and has been introduced over most of the United States and Canada and such places as France, Germany, South Africa, and Hawaii.

Largemouth black bass spawn in the spring, more or less in the same way as do smallmouth. The nest may be located on muddy areas, however, in which case the adhesive eggs are laid on the roots of aquatic plants, on sticks, or on other objects besides stones. The male guards his school of young fish until they are an inch or more in length; that is, for many days he "herds" them and drives off possible enemies. There may be four thousand or more young in such a school, so the father has no small task in watching over all of them. Having attained a size of about an inch, the young lose their tendency to school and become solitary—until winter time when they gather together again in the deeper parts of their home waters, as do many of the black basses and sunfishes when the water becomes cold.

The record largemouth black bass ever taken with hook and line weighed twenty-two and one-quarter pounds and was thirty-two and

one-half inches long. Specimens weighing twenty-five pounds have
been reported.

It is generally believed that most fishes can distinguish colours, but
in the largemouth black bass we have definite indications of this faculty.
One investigator was able to train the largemouth to distinguish
between red or yellow and the other primary colours quite easily.
Green and blue were more difficult for the fish to tell apart. The
careful attention fishermen pay to the colour of their flies may therefore
be very worth while.

The Pumpkinseed, *Lepomis gibbosus*, has provided many a boy with
his first fishing experience. Found almost everywhere through its
range, a ready taker of all sorts of bait—even when the bait hides a
bent pin—and an excellent panfish, the pumpkinseed is a beginner's
gamefish second to none. It bites most of the year and can even be
successfully fished through the ice in some localities. Pumpkinseeds
are found in a variety of habitats, but most frequently in the weedy
parts of ponds, lakes, and streams. They occur naturally from southern
Canada to South Carolina, west to Pennsylvania, Iowa, and the Dakotas,
but have been introduced into California, British Columbia, and
France, among other places.

The pumpkinseed belongs to the family Centrarchidae, a group
that also includes the black basses, sunfishes, crappies, rock bass,
warmouth, and Sacramento perch—in all about thirty species. This
family is confined to North America, no member of it existing anywhere else unless introduced there by man. The largest species is the
largemouth black bass; the smallest, the pygmy sunfish from the south-
eastern United States, which is adult when about one inch long.

As in the great majority of sunfishes, the male pumpkinseed builds
a nest and takes care of the eggs and young. One of the most characteristic views of North American fish life consists of a colony of male
pumpkinseeds, each on his easily discernible, round nest, all closely
arranged along some sunlit, shallow, sandy or rocky area near the
shore of a pond or lake. Breeding takes place during the late spring
or early summer, and, as a true member of the sunfish family, the
male pumpkinseeds actively build and court only when the sun shines
brightly.

The male constructs the nest by fanning vigorously with his tail.
At the same time, by rapidly backing water with his pectoral fins,

he prevents the forward motion that would ordinarily result from this action. Since he rotates through a complete circle while keeping his head up and more or less over the same spot, the result is a circular, cleaned or excavated area, with a diameter just about twice the length of the fish. After the eggs are laid and hatched, the male does not guard his offspring very long, as the black basses often do.

Similarity in reproductive habits among the sunfishes is undoubtedly one of the many reasons why so many of them hybridize in nature. For example, the pumpkinseed naturally crosses with the warmouth and the green, yellowbelly, longear, bluegill and orangespotted sunfishes. The hybrids produced are perfectly healthy fish with a rate of growth more rapid than that of their parents, but they are all sterile.

PUMPKINSEED ON PATROL

The pumpkinseed, found in many parts of the United States, is a fish that is easy to catch, and hence is popular with the novice fisherman. Its breeding habits are most interesting —the male clears a round area at the bottom of shallow water simply by fanning with his tail and then, as pictured above, guards the eggs deposited there by the female.

The food of the pumpkinseed is quite varied, and includes principally insects and their larvae, snails and small crustaceans like water fleas, together with lesser amounts of worms, leeches, tiny fishes, freshwater sponges, and aquatic vegetation. Although they have been known to live more than twelve years in captivity, pumpkinseeds never grow very large, either in tanks or in nature. They rarely if ever exceed nine inches in length or attain one pound in weight.

[12-15]

The mouth of the largemouth black bass extends back past the eye, so its name is quite appropriate. Its range originally extended from northern Canada through the Great Lakes and Mississippi River systems to Florida and north-eastern Mexico, but the fish has been extensively transplanted. A school of newly hatched young may number more than 4,000 and their father has no small task in watching over all of them. Once they grow to about an inch in length, the young lose the tendency to school and become more or less solitary. Largemouths weighing 25 pounds have been reported. *See page 1532*

[12-15A]

The family name "sunfish" is generally applied to the smaller members, many of which are brightly coloured. The dozen or so species are native to the United States east of the Rockies, but they have also been introduced successfully into other areas. Many sunfish are used in the pond culture of larger fish which feed upon them. In general, the spiny-rayed fishes are considered the peak development of present-day forms—the highest point of a whole line of evolutionary progress. *See page 1526*

[12-16]

An excellent panfish about nine inches long and weighing less than a pound, the pumpkinseed is the "beginners gamefish". It readily takes all sorts of bait, even that presented to it on a bent pin, and bites most of the year. Pumpkinseeds occur naturally from southern Canada to South Carolina and west to the Dakotas, and while they are found in a variety of habitats, they mostly frequent the weedy parts of the ponds, lakes and streams. True members of the sunfish family, the males actively build their nests and court the females only when the sun shines brightly. *See page 1533*

[12-16A]

The yellow perch of the lakes, ponds and the quiet parts of the streams of eastern North America furnish both commercial and sports fishermen with a highly prized catch. Millions of pounds of these fish are taken commercially in the Great Lakes region each year. The largest specimen reported weighed a little over four pounds, but the usual maximum weight is closer to one pound. Transplantations of yellow perch have not been too successful. The perches, together with the pikeperches and darters, make up a family which is represented in northern Asia and all of Europe except Spain and Portugal. The vast majority of the species, however, are found in North America east of the Rocky Mountains. *See page 1527*

Trees and How
to Know Them

MOST ADULTS seem to take trees for granted, but in the child's world they loom large. They are natural play equipment, to be climbed for fruit or for fun. City children are doubly grateful for them in summertime, when the hot sun blisters the pavements and the only comfortable place to play is under widespread, sheltering leaves.

There are other reasons for appreciating trees—because they give homes to the birds and squirrels, and yield to man the wood that he uses in so many ways. Even a young child cannot remain unmoved by the beauty of the trees: the majesty of their boughs and rugged bark, the changing colours of their leaves, the splendid bounty of their fruit, blossoms, and cones. No wonder that most children love the trees and delight in telling the seasons by these living calendars.

Tree Rings and What They Tell Us. You can find the record of a tree's growth in the trunk or a branch that has been cut across. There, in the wood, are the rings that mark each year of its life. In adding to its girth the tree depends on a layer of cells called "cambium", which lies just inside the protective bark. Each year the cambium builds a layer of bark on its outer side and a layer of wood on the inner side.

During spring and early summer, when conditions for growth are most favourable, wood cells develop. During late summer and early autumn, new though somewhat smaller cells are still produced. During the winter, growth stops entirely. When it resumes once more with "spring wood" next to "autumn wood", the contrast between the two kinds of wood produces a line around the trunk. This line we know as the "annual ring".

How Trees Record Their Autobiographies. In a sense the annual rings are the biography of the tree—wide spaces between rings indicate good growing years, whereas narrow spaces tell of seasons of drought or other climatic conditions unfavourable to growth. A series of rings with little space between them at the centre of the trunk, changing to wider-spaced rings toward the bark, might also be a clue to improved growing conditions. The thinning out of surrounding trees, for example, would provide more sunlight and the roots would have less competition for the water and minerals of the soil.

Annual growth rings are common to most of the trees that grow in northern Europe. But in some regions, such as the rainy tropics, there is no distinct growing season. There tree growth is constant, and the wood has a more uniform structure instead of showing annual rings.

When these trees are sawn into boards they do not show the intricate grain that our trees do; what we call the "grain" is simply the annual growth rings sawn lengthwise.

WATCHING A TREE DEVELOP

In attaining its height, a tree does not merely stretch upward. If you observe one from the time it is a sapling until it is a mature tree, you will see that the height of the lowest limb always stays at exactly the same distance from the ground. It gains height as a result of "leaders" at the top of the tree.

Buds—New Life for the Tree. If you open a bud from the tip end of a branch in wintertime, you will find tiny but perfectly formed stems, leaves, and perhaps clusters of flowers. Many trees produce all these in the same bud; others, like the apple and elm, have twigs and leaves in one type of bud, flowers in another. The buds, folded neatly and tightly, are protected by scales that overlap like tiles on a roof.

In the spring you can see the buds open when the scales are cast off and the new twigs lengthen and form new side branches. On most trees the new twigs are only a few inches long, but on some the growth is more noticeable.

How to Grow Tree Buds Indoors. Children can observe this unfolding at close range by putting a few twigs of different kinds of trees into vases partly filled with water. Collect them in the autumn after the leaves have been shed, and cut them carefully with a sharp knife. Through the winter, change the water each week and rinse the twigs in cool water to keep the bud scales fresh and clean—a task performed out-of-doors by winter rains and snow.

If you keep the twigs in a warm, fairly dark place, the buds will enlarge before those on the trees outdoors. When the buds seem almost ready to burst, they should be moved to a sunny window.

Trees Have Their Own Birthday Candles. Trunks are not the only parts of trees that have growth marks. Branches and twigs have them too, and you don't have to cut down a tree to see them. Every year a bud leaves a little circle of scars as it casts off its scales. Consequently the distance between every two circles of scars on the branch shows the growth achieved in a year's time. An imaginative child will enjoy likening the bud scars to birthday candles—by counting them he finds the age of any twig.

Bursting at the Seams. The child who makes a habit of observing some of the details of tree structure will soon notice that while young trees have smooth bark, that of older trees is furrowed and frequently sheds untidily. This also is caused by growth; as the girth of the trunk increases, the constant pressure causes the bark to split. A special layer of cells in the bark forms new corky layers that patch the damaged parts but do not smooth the "wrinkles" that have formed. Trees, like people, often look their age.

How Trees are Nourished

Though we cannot see a tree obtain its food in the same way that we can watch an animal feed, we can observe to some extent how the leaf "factories" secure the materials with which they work. Put a leafy twig into ink and you will see how the colour is carried up through the wood into the leaves. The minerals and water taken from the earth by the rootlets are carried in much the same way up the larger roots, on up into the sapwood of the trunk, and out through the branches and twigs to the leaves.

When you look carefully at the leaves you can see many veins that serve as channels for spreading water and minerals. From these raw materials, and with the help of sunlight, the leaves produce a sugary liquid that travels back to the trunk and through the fibres of the outermost layer beneath the bark to all parts of the tree to nourish it.

STORING FOOD

The work of making food and distributing it, goes on throughout the spring and early summer. By midsummer the tree has achieved most of its growth for the year and it can begin to store extra food in its trunk, branches, twigs, and roots. During the winter the tree rests; the following spring the reserve food is available to help buds open and new leaves can begin to grow.

The Most Famous Tree Food of All. At this point maple sugar and maple syrup come into our story. In North America they are processed from the sap of the maple tree—but what makes that sap so deliciously sweet? As it surges through the maple trees in springtime, the sap dissolves the sugar they have stored up. Thus sugar and sap flow out together into containers the local people have mounted under holes they make in the trunks. Boiling does the rest.

Why Leaves Change Colour and What Makes Them Fall

As children first notice the reds and yellows about the time of the first cold snap, they often conclude that frost causes the leaves to change from green to bright autumn colouring. As it happens, frost is not the cause, though lower temperatures do have some bearing on the change. With the coming of colder weather the earth starts to harden, and the trees are no longer able to draw much water from it.

Lacking water, the green pigment of the leaves begins to fade, and is gradually replaced by yellow and orange pigments that have been present all along, but in smaller quantities than the green. Red colouring has a different origin. It is formed in the cell sap by the same sort of "dye" that colours red cabbage and beets. You can look for lovely red displays on Virginia Creeper and other North American plants in parks and gardens.

This autumn colouring of the leaves occurs only in broad-leaved trees. The narrow thick leaves of conifers retain their green pigment and persist for some years; for this reason they are called "ever-green".

How Leaves Die and Drop Off. While the leaves are changing colour, a thin corklike layer of cells develops between the leaf stems and the twigs to which they are fastened. This layer of weak tissue reduces or shuts off completely the flow of sap to the leaf. This not only contributes to the death of the leaf—it also weakens its attachment so that it falls at a slight breeze or even by reason of its own weight.

How Knots and Knotholes Are Formed

Trees Prune Their Own Branches. Children often have the opportunity to watch trees being pruned in city parks or on suburban lawns. But they are surprised to learn that trees growing under natural conditions are also pruned. The trees do this pruning themselves! One process, called natural pruning, works like this: lower branches become undernourished because excessive shade prevents their leaves from manufacturing food, with the result that these branches die and drop off.

In willows, poplars, and other trees, layers of weak tissue, similar to those that cause leaves to fall, form somewhere along certain branches—sometimes at the base. After a while the branches break off, even though many fresh leaves may still be attached to them. This process is known as self-pruning.

Knotholes and Peepholes. When a branch is lost to a tree by pruning, the remaining short stump of branch eventually becomes overgrown by the trunk. If the tree is felled and cut for timber the end of the branch shows up as a knot. In cases where the branch was quite dead when it dropped from the tree, the knot is a dead one and falls out readily, leaving a knothole—a boon to many a child who wishes to peep through a board fence.

The Underground Life of Trees

Trees vary in many respects, but all kinds are alike in being made up of two main parts. Every tree has a trunk and a crown— or head—which is made up of branches and spray (the term used for its great mass of twigs). We can easily see this part of the tree, but there is another big section which is concealed.

Below the Surface. The root system of a tree is often so extensive that its size would equal that of the crown if this upper part were somewhat compressed. The roots of some species grow almost straight down; other species have roots extending outward close to the surface of the ground. There are trees in some parts of the world with roots many times as widespread as their branches!

Sometimes roots that have pushed partly above the surface help a child to picture the extent of a root system—or he may come upon an uprooted stump to which roots are still attached. City youngsters occasionally see work being done on road surfaces or watch the installation of pipes under pavements which uncovers or cuts into the roots of shade trees. They may well be impressed by the amount of abuse the trees will take; yet there are limits to the damage that a tree can stand.

Repairing Injured Roots. Often the injured roots require treatment. Sometimes it is enough to trim away the ragged edges; in other cases the broken sections should be removed completely. If any considerable amount of root material is taken away when a tree is transplanted, the crown should also be trimmed. This reduces the needs of the foliage for food and water for a time while the root system can no longer do its full part in providing them.

Keeping a Tree Biography

Once a child has a general understanding of tree growth, he will very likely enjoy keeping a record of one particular specimen. Choose a tree fairly near home so that he can observe it often: weekly in the spring and autumn and every two weeks in summer and winter. If he looks at it closely for just a few minutes at a time, he will see the developments there have been: buds noticeably larger, buds opening, flowers blossoming, fruits forming, and so on through changing leaf colours to bare branches.

Insects found on the tree, birds nesting in it, or squirrels using it for their home—these are all part of the story. Such a record kept in a notebook may be illustrated with a few sketches of the tree's changing silhouette, its leaves, flowers, or fruit. At the end of the year the youngster is quite sure to have felt something of the fascination of first-hand observation, and to have an increased interest in all trees.

How to Recognize the Trees

Certain trees have something so special about them that children have no trouble remembering them. The drooping form of the weeping willow, the bark of the silver white birch—these are quite unforgettable. However, you will find dozens of trees in your own neighbourhood that look more or less like many others. It would be rash to conclude that it is quite impossible to recognize them all: there are numerous ways in which each reveals its name to us.

The number of different kinds of trees which occur naturally in Great Britain is not very great; many others, however, have been introduced from other temperate parts of the world. In the following pages both the wild and cultivated members of each natural group are considered together, so that comparisons are made between close relatives.

Over the years that scientists have been studying trees there has developed a standard way of referring to the groups into which they can be arranged. Each distinct kind of tree is called a species;

a group of closely related species is a genus—just as with animals where, for example, all cat-like animals (lion, tiger, leopard, etc.) are grouped in the genus Cat. Each of the groups which follow therefore will correspond to what the scientist calls a genus, and the differences you will be able to look for will be those between species.

OAKS—GRANDEUR, STRENGTH, ENDURANCE

Traditionally, the oak is *the* tree of Britain. Most children will know it for its shiny ovoid fruits, called acorns, in their little rough

"GREAT OAKS FROM LITTLE ACORNS GROW"

The ruggedly noble proportions, the long life and the durable timber have given the oak a special place in the popular imagination of the British. It also has a close connection with our history, for it was used in famous sailing ships as well as in ancient buildings.

cups. The tree is widespread over Britain, and in southern England and the Midlands it is the main tree of the woodlands. Old specimens in the open have thick, short trunks and gnarled, twisted branches, and such old oak trees are often so well-known locally that they are given individual names.

The Common Oak is only one of two British oaks; the other is the Durmast Oak, and, though they are similar, the distinctions should be recognizable with practice. They both have lobed leaves and acorns, but there are differences in detail. The leaves of the Common Oak have small ear-like projections from their blades alongside the leaf stalk on each side; the Durmast Oak's leaf-blades taper evenly into the stalk. The acorns of the Common Oak are set on distinct stalks at least two inches long, where those of the Durmast Oak cluster close on the twig with hardly any stalk at all. And they are said by some observers to differ in other ways: the Durmast to be taller and straighter, with more sharply pointed buds. What do you think? Do the trees with longly stalked acorns always have blunt buds?

You may be able to find our two oaks growing together if you are in the Midlands or north of England. In south-east England, however, the Durmast Oak is much the less common of the two; in the west and north of Britain it is the more common.

There are many other kinds of oak in the rest of the world. They occur all over the north temperate region, especially in North America, and there are others again in tropical Asia. You may be able to find some of the North American ones in parks and gardens. Another to look out for is the Holm Oak or Evergreen Oak, which comes from the Mediterranean. An easy one to recognize is the Turkey Oak from south-eastern Europe: its acorn cups are covered with tangled strands, giving them a mossy appearance.

In Europe the oak has long been prized for its excellent timber. All over England, old houses can be found with great beams of oak still as strong as when they were built in. The texture of the grain gives a special beauty to furniture in which it is used; cut in certain ways it shows a unique mottled pattern known as "figuring". Every child will know how important shipping has been in the history of Great Britain; the ships which first carried Britain's trade and influence round the world were built of oak.

SYCAMORE AND MAPLE

Many children will know the fruits of the sycamore: each of the two leathery round parts has a ribbed wing extending outwards from it. Broken apart, the wing and its half-fruit fall in a fascinating, spinning spiral. Such fruit characterizes another north temperate genus, the Maples, of which the tree we call sycamore is one.

The sycamore is a large tree with smooth grey flaking bark. The twigs in winter can be recognized by their smooth surface and the large green pointed opposite buds with distinct light scars beneath. In spring or summer the tree shows dense drooping tassels of small yellowish flowers. The leaves are large, often more than six inches across, with five-toothed lobes.

We have so far referred to our trees as being of two kinds: those occurring naturally wild or those introduced for cultivation. The sycamore is an example of a third status having been introduced long ago but now spread by itself into wild habitats: we refer to such trees as having become naturalized. Further on the Horse Chestnut is mentioned. This is also an introduced tree, but has hardly spread at all into natural habitats. When you compare its fruit with that of the sycamore you may be able to guess one of the reasons for this difference in their behaviour.

When you have learned to recognize the sycamore you will find its British relative, the Common Maple, makes an interesting comparison. It is much smaller, of course, even when fully grown, but you will need to observe some details to be sure of distinguishing it. The leaves are roughly the same shape, but only half the size, and the teeth on the margin are larger. The winged fruits are also similar, but the two wings of a pair extend directly away from each other, not as in the sycamore, where they have nearly a right angle between them. If you see a maple in flower you will know it at once because the bunch of flowers is short and stands erect.

THE LONDON PLANE—TREE OF THE TOWN

Now we come to a tree which is neither introduced nor native. It is the result of the chance cross-breeding of two introduced plane trees, one kind from North America and one from Asia Minor. A

THE SYCAMORE

Originally from central Europe, this tree can be found all over Britain. The winged half-fruit, if planted, will soon grow into a new tree, but many of the sycamore trees one sees in the countryside are self-sown. The leaves sometimes bear black spots caused by a fungus.

plant of this kind, a mixture of species, we call a hybrid. The London Plane therefore has no native habitat; it is domesticated like the household cat. It is ideally suited to the towns where we plant it because the bark, at least while the tree is young, scales off in large patches, taking the dirt with it. The trunk has a gay, if irregular mottled appearance. The five-lobed leaves are somewhat like those of the sycamore, but the teeth on the margin are much fewer. The trade mark of the London Plane, as with all planes, is the way it flowers and fruits. Early in the year, round balls of flowers on long stalks appear, and these become fruits later in the year.

The dangling balls of old fruits can still be seen for some time after the leaves have fallen.

We are lucky that the London Plane manages so well in the smoky atmosphere of our towns, especially as its leaves are fairly widely spread, and therefore cast a soft, enjoyable shade.

AMERICAN PLANE TREE

This is one of the parents of our London Plane, which is similar but usually has two balls of flowers on the dangling stalk. American children call their plane the Buttonball-tree. The London Plane is famous for managing so well in the smoky atmosphere of cities; and for the way in which patches of bark scale off.

THE LIME

In contrast to the London Plane, the lime does not manage well in towns. It has somewhat sticky leaves which collect the grime in the air. There are three kinds of lime tree native or naturalized in Great Britain, but a beginner will not find it easy to distinguish them. The one called the Common Lime is a garden or roadside tree and, like the London Plane, is thought to be a hybrid. Its parents are the large-leaved lime of western England and Wales and the small-leaved lime of the Midlands and southern England.

The limes are regularly branched trees with rounded crowns; the foliage is rather dense but a recognizable pale green in colour. The leaves themselves are distinctly heart shaped and evenly toothed all round the margin. The flowers and fruits are not conspicuous, but they do have a unique feature: they are set on a stalk that branches from the centre of a narrow, wavy, pale-green wing. The wing acts as a parachute for the fruits when they are ripe, the whole apparatus falling together from the twig.

If you want to learn to recognize the different kinds of lime trees you will have to preserve some leaves and fruits and compare their size, hairiness and the ridging on the fruits. See what you can find out for yourself! The Common Lime has leaves about three inches across, with few hairs on the blade beneath, and its fruits are only moderately ridged; in these features it is intermediate between the other two.

ELMS—STATELY GIANTS

There are a number of elm trees native to Great Britain. Most of them can usually be recognized from their leaves alone. They are not unusual in shape—oval, with sharp points and saw-toothed margins —but the veins are unusually regular and evenly spaced as they run out from the midribs. Most useful of all as a clue is their lopsidedness: one side of leaf is usually larger than the other, and extends farther down the stalk—a most curious feature.

You can find elm trees all over Britain, though they do not really flourish in mountainous areas in this country. The first two to learn about are the Wych Elm and the English Elm. Both are large trees, well over one hundred feet tall when mature; they tend to lose their

THE ELM—GRACEFUL SHADE TREE

Many trees derive their graceful charm from their foliage, but the elm has a handsome
rugged shape as well. Middle-aged specimens which have retained their lower boughs
combine branched strength with a delicate tracery of smaller twigs. Elms sometimes have
lumps on the trunk, called burs, which provide timber with a beautiful mottled grain
used in decorative panelling.

lower branches, giving them a lumpy appearance with a huge spreading
crown high up.

The small flowers of elms occur in tufts along the twigs and would
not be conspicuous except that they come out before the leaves. The
fruits are very characteristic: the small flattened body is surrounded

by a wing of nearly the same colour, so in summer you can see them like bunches of pale green halfpennies all over the tree.

The Wych Elm is the more widely spread of the two elms, it alone occurring wild in Scotland and Ireland. Its leaves are large, as much as six inches or more long and over three inches wide, and their upper side is roughly hairy. The winged fruits are nearly an inch long, and are longer than broad with the seeds almost central. With a name like Wych Elm you can guess this tree has been the subject of various superstitions, but so have many of our trees, and no one knows for sure if "Wych" is directly connected with "witches".

The English Elm is perhaps the best-known tree of the countryside. Its tall, irregular outline will soon become familiar to you. The leaves are smaller than those of the Wych Elm—about three inches long and two broad; they are rough above and softly hairy beneath. The fruits are smaller, too—little more than half an inch across—and they are much more nearly circular than those of the Wych Elm, with the seed set near the notch at the top.

The English Elm has in the last few years acquired the reputation of being a dangerous tree. In high winds, its large boughs may break off and cause harm, but it is not yet clear if this is due to weakening by disease or whether it is an intrinsic character of the tree. The disease, called Dutch Elm disease, has indeed become more prevalent in recent years, but the many elm trees planted a hundred years ago are reaching maturity, so it is hard to tell. It would be a pity if the possibility of the tree being at fault should cause people to cease planting it; the danger can be avoided by removing the heavier lower branches from time to time.

THE POPLARS—A MORE DIFFICULT GROUP

All over Europe can be found avenues of tall, erect trees with short trunks and long narrow crowns. These are Lombardy Poplars, and their shape is a unique characteristic. Mature specimens may be eighty to ninety feet tall, and only ten feet across. It has been planted along roads in this country, and its use is increasing, so it is a tree to look out for. Like all poplars, the flowers appear before the leaves in small pendulous tassels called catkins; some are male with stamens only, some female with an ovary. In summer, you will have to learn

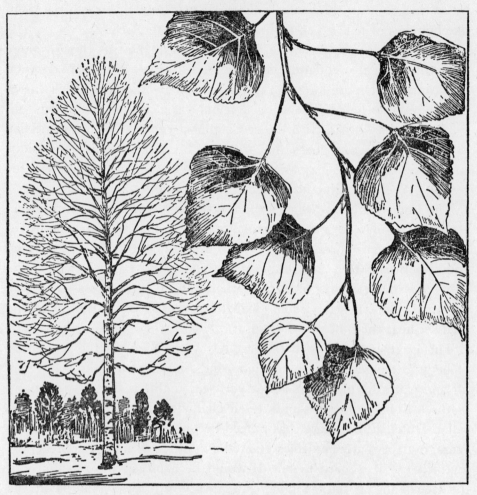

THE RESTLESS FOLIAGE OF THE ASPEN

The slightest breeze sets in motion the foliage of this poplar. Its dark green leaves, which turn clear gold in autumn, are attached by long ribbon-like stalks. The appearance and sound of the quivering leaves have made the tree the subject of various unhappy legends. The aspen is found in many countries.

to recognize the poplars from their leaves, which alternate on the stems, and are triangular or heart-shaped, moderately large, with longish stalks, toothed margins and darkish green upper surfaces.

Another easy poplar to recognize is the Aspen which grows in the open into a regularly shaped tree of moderate size with grey bark. The leaves vary a good deal in size, but always have a very long stalk —as long as the blade or longer; these stalks are flattened sideways, so the slightest breeze sets the leaves fluttering. The margins of the leaves are very shallowly lobed; the leaves are wavy-edged, so to speak.

The aspen is a very widespread tree, being found all the way across Europe and Asia to Japan and southwards across the Mediterranean to Algeria. In Britain it is commoner in the north and west. Its male catkins are quite large, about three inches long, and the reddish anthers make them look like brightly coloured caterpillars on the tree in springtime.

When you have seen the Lombardy Poplar and the aspen you will be able to recognize the other poplars by the similarity of their leaves. Quite a number have been introduced, and some have become natural-ized in Britain. Three which you should find easy to remember by name, if not identify, are called White Poplar, Grey Poplar and Black Poplar.

They are all medium-sized, bushy-topped trees which, either wild or planted, are especially common in southern Britain, most often in low-lying, wettish places. Though they are closely related, you can begin to distinguish them by their leaves.

White Poplars have profuse tangled hairs on the lower surfaces of their leaves, looking like a cover of white felt, and they are two inches or more long, often lobed as much as plane or sycamore leaves. Black Poplar leaves are triangular or narrowly heart-shaped, with fine teeth round the margin, but no lobes and no white felt beneath. As you may guess, the Grey Poplar has leaves which are more or less grey beneath, because the hairiness is less thick than in the White Poplar.

The thin felt wears off the leaves quite quickly, so some leaves on a tree become green on both surfaces. Grey Poplar leaves are roughly the same shape in outline as those of the Black Poplar (narrowly heart-shaped), but the margins have the shallow lobes of those of the aspen instead of the Black Poplar's fine teeth.

One other poplar to be mentioned is a hybrid. It is the Black Italian Poplar, which is quite common in Britain, more so even than the Black Poplar. It is a vigorous tree, planted both by farmers for its shade and by gardeners for its beauty, and able to spread on its own account even into quite wild habitats. Its leaves are similar to those of the Black Poplar, but more nearly heart-shaped, squared off at the stalk and fully rounded to the shorter point.

WILLOWS—GENERALLY FOUND NEAR WATER

The willows are very difficult to sort out, and at first you will do well to recognize them collectively. Like the Poplars, their flowers are in catkins; the males and females are on separate trees. They often have dark bark, and although the leaves are of different shapes they are most often narrow and with finely toothed margins.

WILLOWS—GENERALLY FOUND NEAR WATER

The willows are very difficult to sort out, and at first you will do well to recognize them collectively. Like the poplars, their flowers are in catkins: the males and females are on separate trees. They often have dark bark, and although the leaves are of different shapes they are most often narrow and with finely toothed margins.

A common willow to look out for is the White Willow, which is a largish tree with grey brown bark. The leaves are very narrow, about three inches long and half an inch wide, the margin regularly and finely toothed. It is a native tree which has also been extensively planted.

Some willows are shrubs rather than trees, with rounder wavy-margined leaves and short fluffy catkins. One of these, which is very common, is the Goat Willow, better known to children as "Pussy Willow".

THE HARDY AND LONG-LIVED BEECH

The sturdy beech, a relative of the oaks, has striking beauty of form, foliage and bark. This hardy and long-lived tree is easy to recognize by its smooth grey bark. The generic name of the beech, *Fagus*, comes from a Greek word meaning to "eat"—perhaps a reference to the tasty beech nut, which makes good eating.

THE BEECH—MAJESTIC WOODLAND GIANT

On the chalk hills of southern England the Beech forms heavily shaded woodlands, but it has been planted elsewhere. The silver-grey bark and the twigs with long pointed buds make it easy to recognize in winter, and in summer the bright green leaves with parallel veins are characteristic. The flowers are small and inconspicuous, but there is no mistaking the fruit; the glossy brown nuts are shed from a hard spiny four-lobed husk. The nuts are called "mast" by country folk, and are eaten with relish by some people.

THE ASH

The trees so far discussed all have simple leaves. The leaves of the ash will enable you to recognize it easily because they are divided up into a series of smaller parts called leaflets. In winter, too, the twigs of the ash give themselves away by their short fat black buds.

The flowers of the ash are produced early, before the leaves, and are quite inconspicuous, consisting of small tufts of stamens in the males or even smaller tufts of stigmas in the female. The fruits are called "keys" because they dangle in bunches on thin stalks. Each contains a large seed at the base with a narrow twisted wing extending from it.

BIRCHES—SMALL AND GRACEFUL

Easily recognized by its white stripping bark, the Silver Birch is one of a large group of northern temperate trees. All are moderate-sized trees, and although the fruits are small, the catkins are a recognizable feature, dangling from the tips of the twigs. They are one or two inches long, and increase in size as they mature. The Silver Birch is often found on heaths, on thin sandy soils with little ground vegetation. It is found all across Europe to Asia Minor and Siberia.

THE MIGHTY WALNUT

A tree that has a really massive appearance when fully grown, with its heavy bole, dark greenish bark and spreading foliage, is the Common Walnut. The value of its timber has caused too many to be felled in recent years, but isolated examples can be found throughout the

THE ASH

Although with little beauty of shape, and hardly holding its leaves long enough to produce any autumn colour, the ash makes up for this by its utility: strength combines with flexibility to make its timber unique. It can be used for tool handles, oars, parts of wagons, ladders, barrels and other things; and in the past it had even more uses from spear shafts to aeroplane struts.

country. The tree grows up to a hundred feet tall, with thick spreading boughs. The winter twigs are stout with rather close-set green rounded buds and triangular scars. They possess a unique feature: if you break the twig across, you will find the pith in the centre has a number of slot-shaped gaps, separated by partitions.

The walnut is another introduced tree, from eastern Europe: it has been valued for its timber here for hundreds of years. The wood is

THE SILVER BIRCH

Long before the arrival of the white man in America, the Indians were using the bark of
another birch for their canoes, and the men of northern Europe long ago made baskets
and even bottles, by closely weaving birch bark in layers. The timber is close grained and
easy to work, and, although it is no longer so much used in furniture, smaller domestic
articles are still made from it.

hard and durable, and that cut from the gnarled base of the tree shows
beautiful patterning when cut into veneers. The trees that produce
nuts for cropping in quantity are special kinds grafted on a common
walnut stock.

The male flowers of the walnut occur in large thick tapering catkins;
the female flowers are solitary at the tips of the twigs. See if you can
observe the four minute white petals of the female flower. The leaves

are compound, like those of the ash, with a series of leaflets on either side of the stalk. The leaflets are regularly elliptic, the ones towards the leaf-apex being larger than those below. If you crush the leaves you will find they give off an unpleasant odour.

The fruits are about the size of plums, round and green. Within the fleshy skin is a hard nut formed of two fused shells within which is a single curiously shaped compartment into which the kernel fits exactly; you will probably know the nuts imported into our shops during the winter. It used to be the custom for people in the country to pickle the young fruits entire. If you gather the fruit from the tree, or from the ground when they fall, you will find your hands a short while later covered with brown stains; this is caused by the tannin in their fleshy coverings.

SOME SMALLER TREES

Most of the trees we have dealt with have been those that grow to some size, but this should not mislead you into thinking that all small trees are merely young ones. Many trees do not grow tall even in old age. Holly, for example, though when cut it forms a shrub, can grow into a small tree, some fifty feet tall. You will find it sticking out of hedgerows all over the country. It has shiny, sharply spiny leaves and bright red berries, that make it a favourite for Christmas decoration. Some trees, perhaps the majority, have only male flowers: that is why the berries are scarce. The holly provides timber, used in making rulers; it is useful as well as decorative.

In districts where the soil is chalky, you will commonly see a small tree with black shining bark and small elliptic, serrate leaves. If it is in fruit you may think you have found a wild plum or damson. The fruits are smaller, only acorn sized, but they are dark blue and shaped like plums. Beware, however: what you have found is the sloe or blackthorn, and its fruits have a bitter astringent juice. This short tree has very tough spines and makes a tangling repellent hedge; it flowers early, with an attractive mass of moderate-sized white flowers.

The sloe is of the same family as the plums, damsons, cherries, almonds and apricots. All these trees have similar fruits but of different sizes and shapes as well as tastes. The leaves have similarities, too; all are more or less elliptical with serrate margins, but again they differ in details. Do try to find their characters and learn to recognize them: to know a cherry by its very shiny bark with the cracks which run round instead of up and down, or to recognize the long tassel of flowers of the bird cherry. Do you know the broad leaves of the apricot, the fine sharp flavour of the wild (Morello) cherry, the beautiful single flowers of the almond or the furry green covering of its fruit? You have only to go out into the country and look to learn a thousand fascinating facts.